METHUEN'S MONOGRAPHS ON CHEMICAL SUBJECTS

*General Editors*

R. P. Bell, M.A., HON. L.I.D., F.R.S.
N. N. Greenwood, D.SC., SC.D.
R. O. C. Norman, M.A., D.PHIL.

# CHEMICAL APPLICATIONS OF RADIOISOTOPES

# Chemical Applications of Radioisotopes

H. J. M. Bowen

M.A., D.PHIL.

*Chemistry Department, The University of Reading*

METHUEN & CO LTD

11 NEW FETTER LANE, LONDON EC4

*First published 1969*

*Printed in Great Britain by*
*Butler & Tanner Ltd, Frome and London*

Distributed in U.S.A.
by Barnes & Noble Inc.

## Contents

# Preface

When writing a monograph of this size on a subject as large as radiochemistry, the chief difficulty has been to know what to leave out. There is no possibility of being comprehensive, so the reader must be forbearing if he finds his own speciality omitted entirely, or only briefly discussed. In particular I have left out the following topics entirely: radioactivation analysis; counting techniques; all studies involving stable isotopes; hot-atom chemistry; radiation chemistry; and the Mössbauer effect. All these topics are the subjects of monographs or reviews which are readily available.

Apart from the first introductory chapter, this book attempts to review the ways in which radioisotopes have been used in chemistry. It is hoped that it will be useful to undergraduates with an interest in radiochemistry, and to graduates wishing to enter the field.

H. J. M. B.

# CHAPTER 1

# Properties of Radioactive Isotopes

## The curie

The unit of radioactivity is the curie (Ci). This was originally defined as the number of radium atoms in one gram of radium which disintegrate every second, but is now defined as $3{\cdot}7 \times 10^{10}$ disintegrations per second. The curie is rather a large amount of radioactivity, and tracer work usually involves amounts of radioactivity of the order of millicuries or microcuries. The number of disintegrations per second, or *absolute activity*, is not very easy to measure, and more commonly the number of counts per second, or *relative activity*, is measured by a suitable counting device. Relative activities are frequently compared in quantitative work with tracers.

## Specific activities and half-lives

Another useful concept is the *specific activity*, which is the activity per gram of a labelled element or compound. In practice, the relative specific activity is widely employed, when the absolute specific activity is unknown. Note that it is possible for a doubly labelled compound to have two independent specific activities.

Radioactive decay is an ideal first-order process. Without knowing anything about the disintegration itself, or the particles emitted, it may be assumed that the rate of decay is proportional to the number of atoms ($n$) left at time $t$, i.e.

$$\frac{dn}{dt} = -\lambda n, \quad \text{where } \lambda \text{ is a constant.}$$

Hence $n = n_0\, e^{-\lambda t}$, where $n_0$ is the value of $n$ at an arbitrary zero of time. Since $n$ and $n_0$ are not readily measured, while the rate of decay $dn/dt$ is recorded by any counting device, we can write:

$$\log\left(\frac{dn}{dt}\right) = -\log(\lambda n_0) - 2{\cdot}303\lambda t$$

and by plotting log $(dn/dt)$ against $t$ we should get a straight line from which we can obtain $\lambda$ from the slope and $n_0$ from the intercept (Fig. 1.1). The experimental plots for simple radioactive nuclides

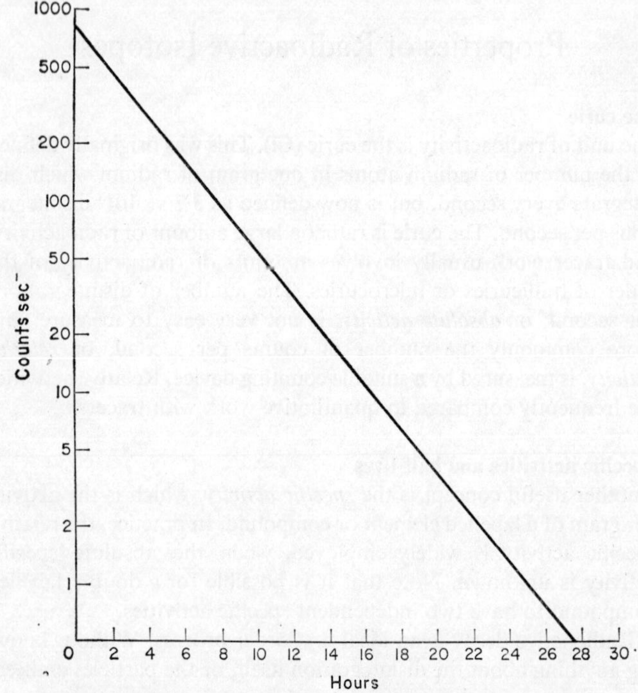


FIG. 1.1. Decay curve of manganese-56; half-life 2·6 hours

are always straight lines, confirming the validity of our initial assumption.

The *half-life* ($t_{\frac{1}{2}}$) of a radioactive nuclide is the time needed for its radioactivity to fall to half its initial value. By substituting $t = t_{\frac{1}{2}}$ and $n = n_0/2$ in the equation above, we see that $t_{\frac{1}{2}} = 0{\cdot}693/\lambda$, so that our plot of count-rate against time can be used to measure half-lives. The half-lives of common radionuclides are given in Appendix 1.

The fraction $f$ of radioactive atoms in an element (or radioactive molecules in a compound) can be calculated from the expression

$$f = 8{\cdot}658 \times 10^{-14} M s t_{\frac{1}{2}}$$

where $M$ is the atomic (or molecular) weight in u, $s$ is the specific activity in Ci g$^{-1}$ and $t_{\frac{1}{2}}$ the half-life in seconds. For example, it is possible to buy elementary phosphorus labelled with phosphorus-32, which has a half-life of 14 days, with a specific activity of 25 mCi g$^{-1}$. Hence the fraction of radioactive atoms in this material is

$$8{\cdot}658 \times 10^{-14} \times 31 \times 0{\cdot}025 \times 14 \times 24 \times 3600 = 8{\cdot}2 \times 10^{-8}$$

so that less than one atom in ten million is actually radioactive.

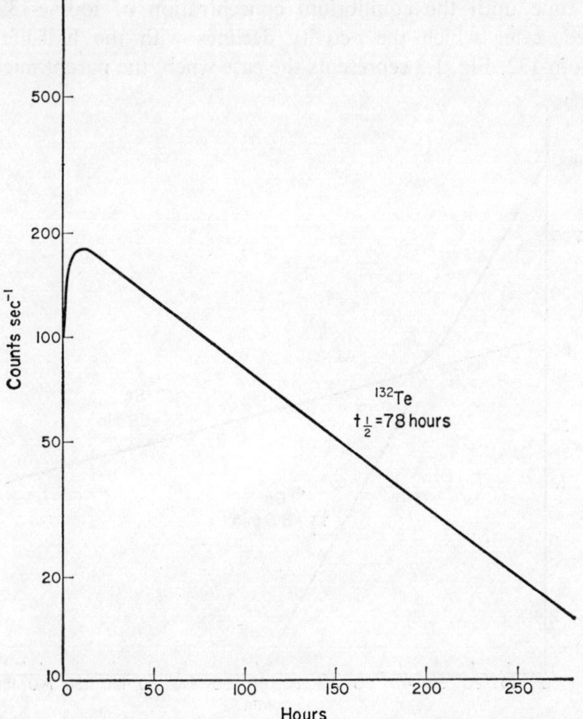


FIG. 1.2. Decay curve of $^{132}Te \rightarrow {}^{132}I \rightarrow {}^{132}Xe$ ($^{132}I$ has $t_{\frac{1}{2}}$ = 2·3 hours)

## Decay chains

If a radioactive nuclide decays to give a daughter nuclide which is itself radioactive, it is said to form part of a decay chain. Long decay chains are known in the heavy, alpha-emitting elements, and among the fission products of uranium. Care must be taken in interpreting the results of experiments involving tracers forming parts of decay chains. If log $(dn/dt)$ is plotted against $t$, the result is not necessarily a straight line. Two possibilities are indicated in Figs. 1.2 and 1.3. Fig. 1.2 represents the case where the parent nuclide has a much longer half-life than the daughter, e.g. 78 hour $^{132}$Te decaying to 2·3 hour $^{132}$I. The total activity *increases* for a short time until the equilibrium concentration of iodine-132 is reached, after which the activity declines with the half-life of tellurium-132. Fig. 1.3 represents the case where the parent nuclide

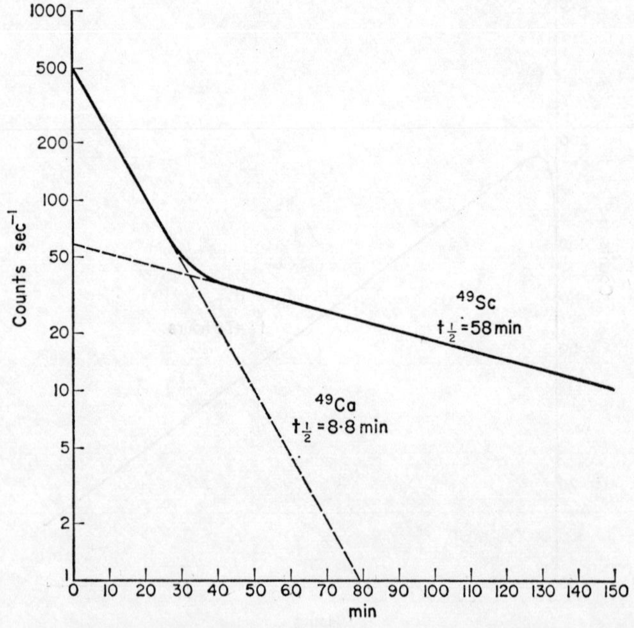


FIG. 1.3. Decay curve of $^{49}$Ca → $^{49}$Sc → $^{49}$Ti

has a much shorter half-life than the daughter, e.g. 8·8 minute $^{49}$Ca decaying to 58 minute $^{49}$Sc. The decay curve can be resolved into two portions corresponding to the two half-lives. After a pair of isotopes such as tellurium-132 and iodine-132 have been separated, it takes about ten half-lives of the shorter-lived isotope before radiochemical equilibrium is established.

## Types of radioactive decay

There are a number of reasons why a nuclide may be radioactive, and as a gross oversimplification we can single out four of these reasons for special mention. Nuclides are likely to be radioactive if they are too heavy, neutron-rich, proton-rich or in excited states.

*Heavy nuclides*, notably most nuclides heavier than bismuth, tend to decay by loss of an alpha-particle. If a nucleus containing A nucleons, Z protons and N neutrons, is designated by (Z, N, A), the process of alpha-decay may be represented by

$$(Z, N, A) \longrightarrow (Z - 2, N - 2, A - 4) + \alpha$$

since the alpha-particle is a helium nucleus with (Z = 2, N = 2, A = 4). For example, the decay of uranium-238 takes place as follows:

$$^{238}\text{U} \longrightarrow {}^{234}\text{Th} + \alpha$$

or

$$(92, 146, 238) \longrightarrow (90, 144, 234) + \alpha$$

Alpha-particles from radioactive decay form densely ionizing but weakly penetrating radiation. Their deflection by electric or magnetic fields shows them to be heavy, positively charged particles and they have well-defined energies in the range 4 to 8 MeV.

*Neutron-rich nuclides*, which are produced by exposure of atoms to a high flux of thermal neutrons in an atomic reactor, decay not by loss of a neutron but by conversion of the excess neutron (n) into a proton ($p^+$), thus:

$$n \longrightarrow p^+ + \beta^- + \nu$$

The proton remains in the nucleus, while the electron ($\beta^-$) and neutrino ($\nu$) are emitted in the process known as beta-decay. Beta-decay may be represented symbolically by:

$$(Z, N, A) \rightarrow (Z + 1, N - 1, A) + \beta^-$$

e.g. $$^{32}P \rightarrow {}^{32}S + \beta^-$$

or $$(15, 17, 32) \rightarrow (16, 16, 32) + \beta^-$$

Beta-particles from radioactive decay form moderately densely ionizing and weakly penetrating radiation. Their deflection by electric or magnetic fields shows them to be light, negatively charged particles. They have a continuous spectrum of energies up to a maximum energy, which is usually in the range 0·1–2 (–10) MeV, since the decay energy is shared between the beta-particle and the neutrino (Fig. 1.4).

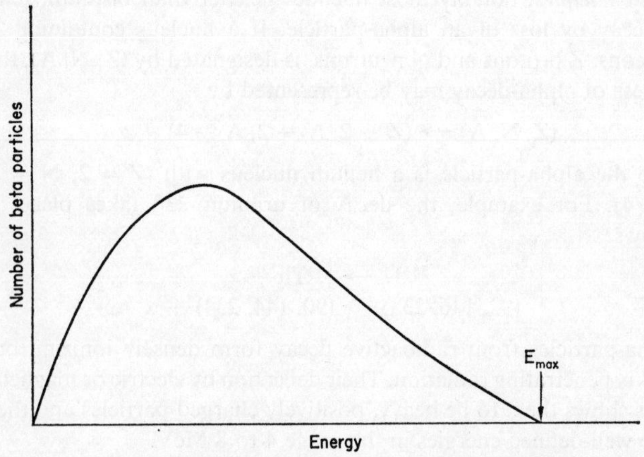


FIG. 1.4. Energy distribution in beta-emission

*Proton-rich nuclides*, which are produced by exposing atoms to a high flux of energetic protons in a cyclotron, mostly decay by conversion of the excess proton into a neutron, thus

$$p^+ \rightarrow n + \beta^+ + \nu.$$

The neutron remains in the nucleus, while the positron ($\beta^+$) and the undetectable neutrino are emitted. This is an alternative form of beta-decay, represented symbolically by:

$$(Z, N, A) \longrightarrow (Z - 1, N + 1, A) + \beta^+$$

e.g. $$^{54}Mn \longrightarrow {}^{54}Cr + \beta^+$$

or $$(25, 29, 54) \longrightarrow (24, 30, 54) + \beta^+ .$$

Positrons from radioactive decay react with electrons in nearby atoms within $10^{-10}$ s to give two 0·51 MeV gamma-photons:

$$\beta^+ + \beta^- \longrightarrow 2\gamma.$$

*Excited nuclides* may be produced in any of the modes of radioactive decay already mentioned, or by excitation with energetic gamma-radiation. A nucleus in an excited state decays by loss of gamma-radiation, and does not change in any other way, i.e.

$$(Z, N, A) \longrightarrow (Z, N, A) + \gamma$$

e.g. $$^{87}Sr^* \longrightarrow {}^{87}Sr + \gamma.$$

Hence emission of gamma-radiation frequently accompanies alpha- and beta-decay, but need not do so.

Gamma-radiation from radioactive decay is sparsely ionizing, extremely penetrating radiation. It is not deflected by electric or magnetic fields, and has a very sharply defined energy in the range 0·1–2 (–7) MeV.

**Detection of radioactivity**

Four of the properties of radioactive radiations are commonly used in their detection (Sharpe, 1964).

(1) *Ionization*

All types of radioactive radiations cause ionization in gases. For example, an average energy of 34 eV is required to ionize a molecule of air at N.T.P., so that radiation with energy of 1 MeV will be able to ionize about $3 \times 10^4$ molecules of air. If the radiation is passed through a gas between the plates of a condenser with a potential gradient of several hundred volts $cm^{-1}$, the electrons produced by ionization are accelerated towards the positive plate and may cause secondary and tertiary ionization. The resulting amplification of the transient electronic currents through the gas is used in such devices as the proportional counter and the Geiger counter. Proportional counters are used for counting alpha- or beta-radiation while Geiger counters are used for beta-counting, and to a lesser extent for gamma-counting.

(2) *Scintillation*

Ionizing radiations cause certain crystals to emit light, which can be amplified and used to operate counting devices. Thus anthracene crystals about 1 mm thick are used to count beta-particles, while crystals of sodium iodide containing about 0·1% of thallium are used to count gamma-rays. The latter crystals may be quite large (e.g. cylinders 15 cm high × 15 cm diameter) in order to absorb energetic gammas efficiently, and are enclosed in a reflecting aluminium sheath except for a window to let out the emitted light. Such scintillation counters are widely used to count gamma-radiation, since the pulse height is proportional to the energy of the radiation.

(3) *Electronic excitation*

Ionizing radiations can excite electrons to the conduction band in semiconducting solids. The energy needed to excite an electron in solid germanium is about 0·76 eV. Large crystals of pure germanium containing traces of lithium are now used for detecting gamma-radiation. They have the disadvantage that they have to be cooled with liquid nitrogen to avoid thermal excitation of electrons, but they have better energy resolution than do sodium iodide crystals.

(4) *Autoradiography*

Ionizing radiations blacken photographic emulsions. This property is especially useful for detecting alpha- and beta-radiation of low energy, as nearly all the radiation is absorbed by the emulsion. Since the sample is made to take its own photograph, this technique is known as autoradiography. It is a good method for the qualitative location of radioactivity in a sample, but is less often used in quantitative work (see Chapter 7).

### Self-absorption

The physical form of a radioactive sample can be very important in any assay process because of self-absorption of the radiations emitted. For example, Fig. 1.5 shows the count-rate from 0·1 $\mu$Ci of

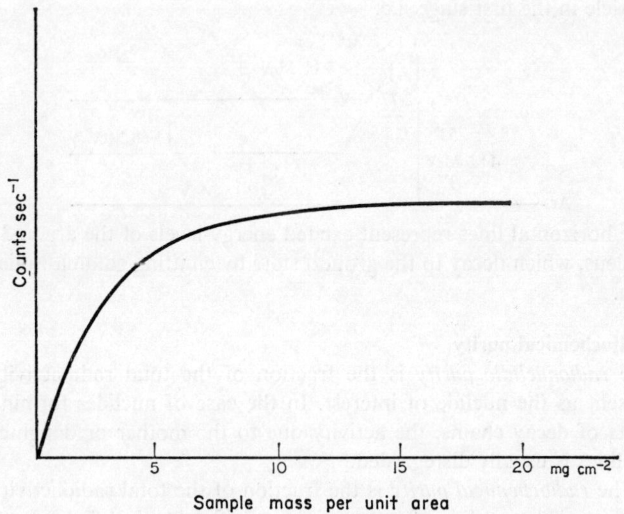


FIG. 1.5. Self-absorption curve for beta-particles from carbon-14

carbon-14 mixed with various amounts of inactive $BaCO_3$. Self-absorption is most important for $\alpha$-emitters and weak $\beta$-emitters, and much less serious for $\gamma$-emitters. It may be allowed for either by plotting an experimental curve such as that of Fig. 1.5, or by comparing the counts from a sample and standard which are as nearly as possible identical in physical shape and form.

### Decay schemes

The actual way in which an individual radioactive nuclide decays may be quite simple, but in most cases it is complex, and the precise decay scheme has not been settled in many of the more complex situations. An example of a simple decay scheme is that of carbon-14, which decays to nitrogen-14 by emitting a beta-particle:

$$^{14}C \rightarrow {}^{14}N + \beta^- + \nu + 0{\cdot}155 \text{ MeV}.$$

A more complex decay scheme is that of chlorine-38, which can decay to stable argon-38 by three paths, each involving loss of a $\beta^-$ particle in the first stage, i.e.

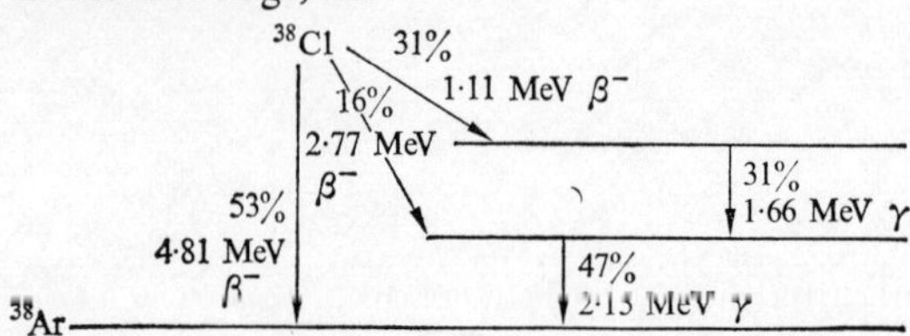


The horizontal lines represent excited energy-levels of the argon-38 nucleus, which decay to the ground state by emitting gamma-radiation.

### Radiochemical purity

The *radionuclidic purity* is the fraction of the total radioactivity present as the nuclide of interest. In the case of nuclides forming parts of decay chains, the activity due to the mother or daughter nuclides is usually disregarded.

The *radiochemical purity* is the fraction of the total radioactivity present as the nuclide of interest in a specific chemical form. Both these types of purity are independent of chemical purity. For example, a synthesis of alanine-C14 might yield a crude product of 70% chemical purity. The radionuclidic purity would be 100% if no radionuclide other than $^{14}C$ was involved, while the radiochemical purity of the L-alanine could not exceed 50% (assuming the impurities were not labelled at all) as an equal amount of the activity would be in the D-alanine produced in the synthesis.

### Radioactive tracers and carriers

A feature of working with radioactive tracers is that the numbers of radioactive atoms concerned are very small, and the amounts of material are often unweighably small. For example, one microcurie of pure phosphorus-32 would give a count-rate of about 3700 counts $s^{-1}$, which is readily detectable in the presence of background radiation of 0·1–0·5 counts $s^{-1}$. One microcurie of phosphorus-32 contains $6{\cdot}3 \times 10^{10}$ atoms, and would weigh only $3{\cdot}3 \times 10^{-12}$ g, so it would not be detected by any analytical balance nor by any conventional method of analysis.

The advantage in being able to detect such very small masses is set off by the difficulties in handling them. For example, a 50 ml beaker has a surface area which can accommodate about $4 \times 10^{15}$ atoms as a layer one atom thick and has a strong affinity for phosphate ions. Hence losses by adsorption on glassware, as well as by dust and filter paper, are potentially very serious.

In order to simplify the handling of radioactive isotopes, it is common practice to add relatively large amounts of inactive isotopes to them. These stable isotopes are known as *carriers*, because they help to carry the radioisotopes through various chemical changes without measurable losses from adsorption by the walls of the apparatus used. The addition of carrier is not always necessary, nor is it desirable in all cases, since it may reduce the specific activity by many orders of magnitude. Occasionally it is possible to use one inactive element as a carrier for the radioactive isotopes of another, as for example in the case of barium and radium. Carriers are employed to remove small traces of radioactive impurities. For example, traces of iron-59 may be removed from a solution of cobalt-60 by making it 6M in hydrochloric acid and then repeatedly adding inactive ferric chloride, oxidizing the solution and extracting it with diethyl ether. When carriers are used to reduce the amount of radioactive impurity which is absorbed during a precipitation, they are known as *hold-back carriers*.

**Assumptions involved in using radioisotopes as tracers**

A basic assumption underlying the use of radioisotopes as tracers is that the *relative proportions of isotopes are unchanged by all physical and chemical processes*. This assumption implies that a radioisotope (or labelled molecule) behaves exactly like the element (or unlabelled molecules) present.

There are several points about this basic assumption which need urther explanation. In the first place, the isotope must have been properly mixed with the carrier. Where physical mixing is involved, it suffices to continue mixing until successive samples have the same specific activity. Chemical mixing may be more difficult, especially for elements of variable valency, and the method of mixing must depend on the reaction which is being studied. For example, in a solution containing potassium permanganate and manganous sulphate, one could label either the permanganate anion or the manganous cation with radioactive manganese-54. In order to label all the manganese present, one would have to oxidize quantitatively to permanganate, or reduce quantitatively to manganese(II), after adding the radioisotope.

Secondly, it is known that the relative proportions of isotopes can be changed both in rate processes and in separation processes under conditions of equilibrium. If this were not so, isotopes could neither be separated nor fractionated, whereas several separations are now carried out commercially. Apart from the special case of hydrogen, whose radioisotope tritium is three times as heavy as the stable isotope protium, the separation of isotopes by physical and chemical processes is inefficient and rarely takes place to an extent exceeding 1%, which is usually within the error of measurement. Even in the case of hydrogen, the separation factor for tritium in most single-stage processes rarely exceeds 10%. Hence our basic assumption is not strictly true, but is usually adequate if measurements are required with a precision not exceeding 1%.

Thirdly, there are physical processes which can change the relative proportions of isotopes present. These include the absorption of either neutrons, charged particles such as protons, or gamma-radiation of high energy. The relative proportions of isotopes could also be changed by raising the temperature sufficiently, but since the temperatures needed to do this are of the order of those of stellar interiors ($10^9$ K), this fact is only of academic interest in the present context.

**Selection of tracers**

In choosing a tracer for any particular application, three points are of paramount importance:

(1) The tracer must truly represent the behaviour of the material

being studied. For example, the only long-lived chemical tracers for water are HTO and $T_2O$, but for many purposes an isotope such as sodium-24 can be dissolved in a sample of water, and used to follow this sample physically. In some cases, for example in tracing proteins, the only labelled material available may be the adduct of a similar protein with $^{131}I_2$. This adduct is obviously an imperfect tracer, but is adequate for some applications.

(2) The half-life of the tracer must be not much less than the duration of the experiment. For example, in studying the chemical reactions of iridium, 19 hour $^{194}Ir$ is generally a suitable tracer. If, however, the problem is to determine the rate of attrition of an industrial iridium catalyst over a six-month period, the isotope of choice would be 74 day $^{192}Ir$.

(3) The radiation emitted by the isotope must be readily measurable under the conditions involved in the desired application. In most applications of radioisotopes in research, the isotope concerned can usually be isolated in a form suitable for Geiger or scintillation counting. This is not true in many industrial applications, e.g. the use of $^{60}Co$ to measure the attrition in the lining of a blast-furnace. In 'remote control' applications of this kind, it is necessary to use an isotope which emits energetic gamma-radiation, since alpha- or beta-radiation would be completely absorbed in the intervening materials.

**Advantages of using radioactive isotopes**

Some advantages of using radioactive isotopes are as follows:

(1) The sensitivity of detection is usually in the range $10^{-16}$ to $10^{-6}$ g.
(2) Radioactivity is easy to locate and assay.
(3) Radioactivity is independent of pressure, temperature, physical or chemical state.
(4) Radioactivity is specific for a tracer even in the presence of identical chemicals.
(5) The precision of counting techniques is usually adequate and can be excellent.
(6) The technique is often non-destructive.

The *sensitivity of detection* or assay has already been mentioned on p. 10. The *simplicity of location* is based on the penetrating nature of the radiation emitted, and on the law relating the intensity of radiation to the inverse square of the distance from a point source of radioactivity.

The *independence of physical and chemical states* has been discussed on p. 12. Advantage (4), specificity, is best illustrated by an example, the measurement of self-diffusion in metallic lead. If two bars of lead are brought into contact, it is impossible to test whether atoms from one bar are diffusing into the other, since all the lead atoms are identical. By labelling one bar with 19 year $^{210}Pb$, transfer of atoms can not only be demonstrated but also measured in a precise manner. The actual *precision* of radioactive assay is well defined, since it is known that the standard deviation of the number $N$ of counts recorded is equal to $\sqrt{N}$. That is, if we have measured 100 counts, the precision is $\pm 10$; with 1000 counts, the precision is $\pm 31$; and with 10,000 counts, the precision is $\pm 100$. In terms of percentage of the counts recorded, these three cases represent 10%, 3·1% and 1% respectively. The percentage precision in an experiment therefore depends on the total number of counts recorded, which in turn depends on the time available for counting, except in the special case where the isotope is decaying very fast.

**Disadvantages of using radioactive isotopes**

Disadvantages in using radioactive isotopes include health hazards, difficulties of waste disposal, isotope effects, radiation effects and the cost of equipment.

Hazards to health often loom large in the imaginations of intending users, but as far as tracer work is concerned they are rarely more serious than the hazards involved in handling chemicals such as concentrated sulphuric acid, arsenic or potassium cyanide. It should be recalled that most tracer work involves submicrocurie amounts of radioactivity in the samples used for assay, and that an adult man contains about 0·15 $\mu$Ci of natural $^{40}K$, together with other natural radioisotopes, in his own body. The largest amount of activity normally handled in a tracer laboratory is 10 mCi. If this is a pure beta-emitter, such as calcium-45 or carbon-14, the glass storage bottle may be adequate protection againt radiation. Gamma-emitters in amounts exceeding 1 mCi should be stored behind 5 to 10 cm of lead shielding, but may be handled for short periods outside the shield. Most radioisotopes are conveniently stored in 30 ml polythene bottles with a capillary outlet; glass containers should be stood in plastic beakers in case of breakage.

In handling radioactive isotopes (or any hazardous chemicals) the following rules should be borne in mind.

(1) Keep all radioactive solutions and apparatus on labelled trays, from which inactive equipment is excluded.

(2) Wear surgical rubber gloves whenever there is a danger of contaminating your hands.

(3) Use forceps or tongs rather than your hands to pick up highly radioactive equipment.

(4) Have labelled radioactive waste-bins, absorbent tissues and plastic squeeze-pipettes ready in case of spills.

(5) When heating or evaporating radioactive solutions, use a fume chamber.

(6) If your laboratory and fume chamber has not got an impervious floor covering, instal one.

(7) When weighing radioactive solids or solutions, use disposable plastic equipment and double containment whenever possible.

(8) Use a simple ratemeter as a monitor to check the contamination of equipment and laboratory clothing after each experiment.

(9) Wear a film-badge to test your exposure to ionizing radiation each week.

(10) Remember that radioactive contamination can usually be removed from impervious materials (e.g. metal, glass, plastic) but is difficult to remove from porous materials such as wood, cloth, paper, plaster or brick.

If radioactive wastes are kept in labelled plastic bins, their disposal rarely presents a grave problem. It is a good plan to have four categories of waste.

(1) *Highly active wastes*, such as aluminium cans from a reactor, or glass bottles which have contained millicurie amounts of reagents, may need storage behind lead for several months.

(2) *Incombustible wastes*, mostly metal or glass, may either be stored until the activity has decayed, or buried in a deep hole.

(3) *Combustible wastes*, mostly paper or plastic, may be stored until the activity is small or negligible and then burned on a metal tray so that the ash may be collected and monitored.

(4) *Liquid wastes* can usually be poured down the drain, but local regulations should be consulted. Most British authorities allow the disposal of up to 50 millicuries per year from a laboratory drain, but by controlled storage it is not difficult to confine the sink disposal to less than 50 microcuries per year. This constitutes a minor hazard because of the tremendous dilution involved – a laboratory may flush $10^5$ litres of water down its drains each day.

*Isotope effects* have already been mentioned on p. 12, where it was shown that it is extremely rare for radioisotopes to behave in a different manner to their carrier element by more than 1%. Isotope effects are largest with tritium, or hydrogen-3.

*Radiation effects* are said to occur when a labelled molecule decomposes because of self-absorption of ionizing radiation. They are particularly important in organic molecules of high specific activity, labelled with pure beta-emitters such as carbon-14 or tritium. Obvious radiation effects include the production of gas in sealed ampoules of radioactive liquids, and the darkening of the glass used for the ampoules themselves. Radiation effects can be minimized by using low specific activities, by dilution with an inert solvent to keep the radioactive molecules apart, and by not storing high specific activity material for long periods. It may be necessary to test the radiochemical purity of some labelled substances immediately before use.

The main disadvantage of tracer work is perhaps the cost of the ancillary equipment required. The costs of radioisotopes vary considerably, but it is possible to buy the most common isotopes in amounts of 10 millicuries for between £5 and £20. Assuming one needs 0·1 microcuries per assay, this gives a potential of $10^4$ assays per £, which is not expensive. On the other hand the assaying equipment will probably cost between £250 and £500, which is comparable with the costs of analytical balances, spectrophotometers, flame photometers and other moderate-sized laboratory instruments. The cost of modifying a laboratory to handle tracer amounts of radioactivity is not enormous. The main outlay is on the impervious floor covering, and on a laboratory monitor, each of which will cost between £50 and £100. The other items needed, such as metal trays, rubber gloves, a few lead bricks, forceps and plastic waste-bins are relatively cheap. A castle of lead bricks can be expensive, but while useful it is not necessary for most tracer work. Highly active solutions may be stored in castles of brick or cement blocks unless space is at a premium, or sunk in small wells in the floor under a heavy lid.

## References

BOURSNELL, J. (1958). *Safety Techniques for Radioactive Tracers*. Cambridge University Press.

BRODA, E., and SCHÖNFELD, T. (1966). *The Technical Applications of Radioactivity*. Pergamon.

DUNCAN, J. F., and COOK, G. B. (1968). *Isotopes in Chemistry*. Clarendon Press, Oxford.

FAIRES, R. A., and PARKS, B. H. (1960). *Radioisotope Laboratory Techniques*. Newnes.

FRIEDLANDER, G., KENNEDY, J. W., and MILLER, J. M. (1964). *Nuclear and Radiochemistry*. Second edition. Wiley.

NEFEDOV, V. D., TOROPOVA, M. A., KRIVOKHATSKAYA, I. V., and SINOTOVA, E. N. (1965). *Radioactive Isotopes in Chemical Research*. Moscow.

SHARPE, J. (1964). *Nuclear Radiation Detectors*. Methuen.

CHAPTER 2

# Physical Applications of Tracers

The applications of tracers to be described here are physical rather than chemical applications; the latter are discussed more fully in succeeding chapters. A 'physical' application is one in which the chemical nature of the radioactive atom used is relatively unimportant, as the nature of the radiations emitted are the major concern. A fuller discussion of many of the items in this chapter can be found in monographs by Jefferson (1957), Kohl *et al.* (1961), Erwall *et al.* (1964), Gardner and Ely (1967) and Broda and Schönfeld (1966).

**Detection of invisible objects**

A very simple physical application involves the detection of invisible objects. For example in the chemical industry it is often necessary to bury a pipe conveying vital materials, so that the course of the pipe, its bends and junctions, are invisible. It is possible to label each bend or junction with a powerful gamma-emitter, such as cobalt-60, so that they can be located with a scintillation counter at a subsequent date. About 200 mCi of cobalt-60 are needed to label an object buried at a depth of 1 metre of soil, so that this application requires more radioactivity than most tracer techniques. In much the same way, the level of liquid in a vertical pipe or cylindrical reactor vessel with opaque walls can be determined very precisely from external measurements. Here the radioactive label may be a small piece of cobalt-60 (~1 mCi) sealed inside a buoyant float, which marks the level of the liquid without contaminating it in any way. For this type of application, the main requirement is an isotope emitting energetic gamma-radiation, and with a fairly long half-life. Cobalt-60 has a 1·33 MeV gamma and a half-life of 5·3 years, while antimony-124 has a more energetic gamma (1·69 MeV) but a shorter half-life (60 days.)

**Mixing processes**

Many operations in both research and industry involve homogeneous mixing as an important step. Mixing may either be carried out in batches or as a continuous process. In either type of mixing, the addition of a radiotracer to one component makes it very easy to test for homogeneity. After the tracer has been added to a batch, the mixture is sampled at various intervals of time, and the activities of samples of equal weight are compared, using a counter of standard geometry. The mixture is homogeneous when samples from all parts of it have the same specific activity. The amount of tracer needed is quite small. For example, 50 mCi of radioisotope is adequate to study the mixing of a ton of many products. At 10% counting efficiency, 1 g samples from the homogeneous mixture would give a count-rate of 11,000 counts per minute, with a standard deviation of $\pm 1\%$. This is equivalent to 50 $\mu$Ci of tracer per kg of mixture on the laboratory scale. Mixing studies have been carried out on a variety of products, such as ceramics, cements, greases, solid propellants, petroleum products and animal feeding-stuffs. In many cases, a single investigation was sufficient to discover the minimum time needed for efficient mixing, thus economizing on the power needed to drive stirring machinery. By using short-lived radioisotopes, such as $^{56}MnO_2$ or $^{24}NaCl$, the contamination of the plant and product was immeasurably small after storage for a suitable period. Thus in the case of $^{56}Mn$, with a 2·6-hour half-life, each 24-hour storage period diminishes the activity remaining to 1/500th part of its initial value. Another advantage of the isotope technique is that it is well adapted to studying the mixing of small weights of material with very large weights of product. For example, cattle feeding-stuffs need to contain at least 8 p.p.m. copper (Schutte, 1964). It may be necessary to add a few p.p.m., i.e. a few grams per ton, of copper to a foodstuff deficient in this element, and it would be very difficult to demonstrate homogeneous mixing without using the tracer technique (Jefferson and Wildblood, 1956; Barker, 1958; Hoffmann, 1960; Cless-Bernert and Duftschmid, 1964).

**Measuring volumes of inaccessible containers**

The volume of any container can be measured by the isotope dilution principle (Hull and Fries, 1956; Hull, Fries and Gilmore, 1965). A common practical problem involves measuring the volume $V$ of liquid in a relatively inaccessible container. In order to do this, we take a small volume $V_1$ of tracer solution and measure its activity $a_1$ using a suitable counter. Add the tracer to the liquid, mix thoroughly, and finally remove a sample of volume $V_1$, equal to the initial volume of tracer used. Measure the activity $a_2$ of the sample using the same geometry as for the initial tracer, and obtain the volume from the expression

$$V = V_1\left(\frac{a_1}{a_2} - 1\right).$$

In most cases $V_1$ is so small in comparison with $V$ that any volume changes on mixing can be neglected. It is, of course, important that the tracer should be completely miscible with the liquid whose volume is to be measured. Thus there is a wide choice of tracers for aqueous solutions, but for liquid hydrocarbons the choice is more limited. In the latter case ethylene dibromide - Br82, tetramethyl germanium - Ge77, tetraethyl tin - Sn113, triphenyl stibine - Sb124, triethylammonium aurichloride - Au198 or palladium acetonyl acetonate - Pd109 are possible tracers with hard beta- or gamma-activities which are more readily detected than are the soft betas from alkanes labelled with tritium or carbon-14.

Volumes of containers can also be measured when liquids are flowing through them at a known rate. Tracer solution is added to the input stream, and the volume calculated from the rate of decrease of radioactivity in the output stream.

Gas volumes can be determined by similar methods using $^{41}Ar$, $^{85}Kr$, $^{133}Xe$ or other inert tracers, which may involve special counting techniques.

**Leak testing**

Leak testing is extremely important in many branches of technology, both for 'sealed-off' units such as electronic valves, metal cans and nuclear fuel elements and for flowing systems such as service pipes, high vacuum lines, pressure vessels and heat exchangers. Sealed-off units may be investigated by sealing a small amount of methyl bromide-Br82 or similar short-lived tracer into the device. One can either check that the activity of the unit decays with the correct half-life, or place the unit in a high vacuum and count any gas which is pumped off (Guéron, 1951). Flowing systems are usually filled with an aqueous solution containing $^{82}$Br, $^{38}$Cl or $^{24}$Na and monitored externally. Leaks will show up as 'hot-spots' above the relatively high background activity, which remain when the solution is run to waste. Vacuum lines may be connected to a gaseous counter while suspected leaks are squirted with a jet of tritium gas. Tritium activity will only register on the counter if gas has diffused into the vacuum line, because the weak beta-activity will not penetrate glass or metal walls.

Special techniques are needed to detect leaks in pipes which are buried in soil, e.g. in chemical plant. In the static method, the pipe is isolated and filled with a solution containing $^{24}$Na for a short time. The tracer will contaminate the soil around leaky spots, which can be found by monitoring after the tracer solution has been washed away. If the pipes are buried more deeply than 1 metre, it is best to draw a scintillation counter, connected to an external ratemeter, through the pipe itself so as to avoid the shielding effect of the soil. If the cable pulling the counter is marked off in metres, the position of the leaks can be easily located. Several dynamic methods have also been evolved to measure leaks in flowing systems, and the current tendency is to automate these methods as far as possible. They are valuable since they may save time and energy in digging up great lengths of buried pipes for conventional leak-testing (Fisher, 1961; Jefferson, 1957; Dore *et al.*, 1953).

**Measurements of fluid flow**

Fluid flow rates can be measured by a variety of techniques (Clayton, 1960; Kohl, Zentner and Lukens, 1961; Erwall, Forsberg and Ljunggren, 1964). The advantages of using isotope techniques include the following:

(1) No obstacles need be introduced into the flowing system to

disturb it. Measurements can even be made through thick walls of pipes.

(2) Dissolved and suspended matter in the fluid do not interfere.

(3) No assumptions are needed as to whether the flow is partially or wholly turbulent.

The tracer used depends on the fluid concerned. For aqueous fluids, $^{24}NaCl$, $Na^{131}I$ or $NH_4{}^{82}Br$ are commonly employed, since none of these are strongly adsorbed by suspended matter. For petroleum products 1,2-ethylenedibromide-Br82 is a readily-obtainable tracer. $^{41}Ar$ or $^{85}Kr$ may be used for measuring gas flow-rates in pipelines: the flow of gas in blast furnaces has been investigated using $^{222}Rn$.

The use of tritium (hydrogen-3) as a label for water and aqueous solutions has been extensively studied. Tritium emits beta-particles of very low energy and requires special techniques for its detection. Nevertheless, by modern techniques one atom of tritium can be detected in the presence of $10^{19}$ atoms of hydrogen-1. Until recent years, fresh rainwater contained about 1 atom of tritium per $10^{18}$ atoms of hydrogen-1, but this natural tritium content has been perturbed by man-made tritium since 1956. Deep ocean water, and some underground waters, contain negligible tritium and are said to be 'old', i.e. buried for more than 10 half-lives, or 120 years (I.A.E.A. Symposium, 1961; Libby, 1961; Carlston, 1964; Israel and Krebs, 1962).

In the *single-injection technique*, $x$ microcuries of tracer are injected upstream. The numerical value of $x$ should be of the same order as the bulk flow-rate measured in $m^3\ s^{-1}$. The stream is monitored at two positions downstream, preferably using ratemeters with recorder read-outs. In this way the times $t_1$ and $t_2$ of maximum count-rate can be fixed at each monitoring position (1 and 2). If the two monitors are $d$ metres apart, the velocity of flow $v$ is given by

$$v = \frac{d}{t_2 - t_1}\ \mathrm{m\ s^{-1}}$$

and the bulk flow-rate can be calculated if the flow takes place through tubes of known cross-section. This method has a precision of about ±0·5%.

In a less precise modification, a single monitor is used at a distance $d$ from the point of injection of tracer. $d$ should be chosen to be about 50 $\sqrt[3]{f}$ metres, where $f$ is the bulk flow-rate in $m^3\ s^{-1}$. The total number of counts $C$ recorded by the monitor, after subtraction of background, is inversely proportional to the velocity of flow $v$, i.e.

$$Cv = k, \quad \text{where } k \text{ is a constant.}$$

For flow in pipelines, $k$ may be obtained by measuring the count-rate from sections of pipe filled with known specific activities of the tracer.

In the *continuous injection technique*, tracer with high specific activity $s_1$ counts $s^{-1}\ l^{-1}$ is continuously injected into the stream at a rate $f_1$ $l\ s^{-1}$. The specific activity $s_2$ is measured downstream after complete mixing has occurred, so that the bulk flow-rate $f_2$ is given by:

$$f_2 = \frac{s_1 f_1}{s_2}\ l\ s^{-1}$$

The rate of injection of activity required is approximately $2{\cdot}5 f_2$ microcuries per second, if $f_2$ is measured in litres per second. This method therefore requires more radioactivity than the single-injection method, but it can be almost equally precise (±1%), and can be used to measure bulk flow-rates in streams of variable or unknown cross-section, such as rivers. For applications to gaseous systems with flow-rates up to 10 kg $s^{-1}$, see Fries (1965) and Fries *et al.* (1965).

In addition to measuring bulk flow-rates and velocities, radio-isotopes are useful for measuring residence times and for studies of recycling. The residence time of any material in a chemical reactor vessel is equal to the volume of the reactor divided by the bulk flow-rate (Hovenkamp, 1966). It can be found by labelling the input stream of material by a single injection of tracer. The output stream is then monitored and the residence time or half-life of the material in the reactor vessel can be calculated. The residence time is one of the most important variables in chemical technology.

When a labelled product is partially recycled, as in sieving operations where the coarse fraction is sent back for regrinding, a single monitor placed at a convenient point will give a damped periodic register of count-rate against time (Fig. 2.1). The rate of cycling can be obtained from the distance between successive peaks, while the fraction recycled is proportional to the area enclosed by the curve.

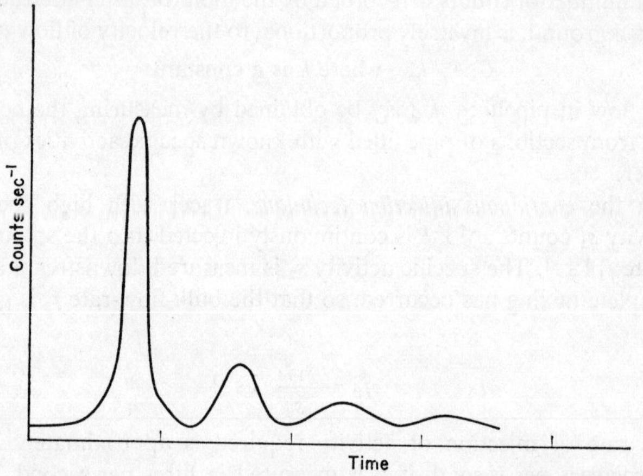


FIG. 2.1. Counting rate obtained when labelled material is recycled

Note that these measurements can be applied not only to fluids, but also to any material which is handled on conveyor belts, or similar flow-systems. If solids are not labelled homogeneously, errors may arise. Small particles may have a larger surface/volume ratio than do large particles, and may therefore have a higher specific activity if labelling is confined to their surfaces.

**Testing filtration techniques**

The effectiveness of filters can readily be tested using tracer techniques. Early methods included the plating of plastic microspheres of known size with gold-198, and testing whether these were retained by bacteriological filters (Seligman, 1954). Alternatively living cells of bacteria or algae (e.g. *Chlorella*), which have a restricted range of sizes, can be made to take up caesium-137; this has been shown to be an irreversible process. The labelled cells then function as test objects for filter media, but the technique is no more sensitive, merely quicker, than conventional studies involving culturing the filtrate in sterile flasks (Ives, 1960).

A more general technique has been suggested, but needs considerable preparatory work. Glass is labelled with a suitable tracer, such as scandium-46 or cerium-144, neither of which are readily dissolved from the exposed surface of the glass. The glass is reduced to a powder by grinding, and the powder is then sieved using a series of graded sieves. The coarser fractions may be used to test relatively coarse filter pads, but the main interest lies in fractions with particle diameters less than 50 $\mu$m, which come through all but the very finest sieves. Most conventional filter media have apertures in the range of 1–50 $\mu$m: particles with diameters of less than 2 $\mu$m are generally said to be colloidal. Glass particles in this size range may be fractionated by careful sedimentation, and still smaller particles can be fractionated by ultracentrifugation. Once labelled particles of known ranges of sizes have been prepared, they can be used to obtain quantitative data on the performance of unknown filter media.

Labelled particles of $^{64}CuO$, $^{65}ZnO$ and $^{24}NaF$, all generated as 'smokes' of colloidal dimensions, have been used to test the efficiency of removal of these substances from industrial effluent gases. Eden and Melbourne (1960) describe how to measure the mean period over which a porous filter retains the liquid flowing through it.

**Measuring rates of attrition**

Tracers can be used to measure the rates of attrition of critical parts in chemical plant: the parts concerned are often invisible and so it is not an easy matter to find out their state of wear by conventional methods. Two examples will be given. The first concerns the rate of wear of the refractory linings of blast-furnaces or steel-making furnaces. Pellets of cobalt-60 metal, or ceramic pellets labelled with the same isotope, are frequently inserted in a number of places in the furnace lining. These can be monitored from outside the furnace, and when the radiation falls in intensity, the lining is known to be wearing thin. In this way the furnace can be operated continuously without the need for shut-downs to examine the linings, and the need for replacing these linings is made evident from external measurements. As a result of the widespread employment of this technique, it is now difficult to obtain supplies of iron and steel which are not slightly contaminated with cobalt-60 (Voice, 1951a and b; Holtzhey, 1962).

The second example concerns the fate of heterogeneous catalysts in industrial plants. During the catalytic oxidation of ammonia to nitric oxide, the platinum–iridium catalyst is not only partially poisoned, but also undergoes a considerable loss in weight. By labelling the catalyst with $^{192}$Ir, it was possible to trace where the missing atoms had travelled inside the plant (Been and Saeland, 1956). Similar studies have been carried out during the hydrogenation of unsaturated oils, using nickel catalysts labelled with nickel-63 (Braier *et al.*, 1965). It has been shown that most solids can be labelled with the inert gas krypton-85, and that surface labelling is a valuable technique for measuring rates of attrition (Cucchiara and Goodman, 1967).

## References

BARKER, R. S. (1958). *Trans. Soc., Glass Technol.*, **42,** 109.

BEEN, U., and SAELAND, E. (1956). *Proc. Int. Conf. on Peaceful Uses of Atomic Energy*, **15,** 170, New York.

BRAIER, H. A., MOTT, W. E., and SCHMID, B. K. (1965). *Int. J. Appl. Radiat. Isotopes*, **16,** 611.

BRODA, E., and SCHÖNFELD, T. (1966). *The Technical Applications of Radioactivity*. Pergamon.

CARLSTON, C. W. (1964). *Science*, **143,** 804.

CLAYTON, C. G. (1960). *Nucleonics*, **18,** no. 7, 96.

CLESS-BERNERT, T., and DUFTSCHMID, K. (1964). *Atomwirtschaft*, **9,** 226.

CUCCHIARA, O., and GOODMAN, P. (1967). *Mater. Eval.*, **25,** 109.

DORE, E. A., JOINER, C. H., PUTMAN, J. L., JEFFERSON, S., and CAMERON, J. F. (1953). *J. Instn. Wat. Engrs.*, **7,** 160.

EDEN, G. E., and MELBOURNE, K. V. (1960). *Int. J. Appl. Radiat. Isotopes*, **8,** 172.

ERWALL, L. G., FORSBERG, H. G., and LJUNGGREN, K. (1964). *Industrial Isotope Techniques*. Copenhagen.

FISHER, C. (1961). *Atomwirtschaft*, **6,** 481.

FRIES, B. A. (1965). *Int. J. Appl. Radiat. Isotopes*, **16,** 35.

FRIES, B. A., HULL, D. E., DUPZYK, R. J., and LAMOREE, D. J. (1965). *Int. J. Appl. Radiat. Isotopes*, **16,** 561.

GARDNER, R. P., and ELY, R. L. (1967). *Radioisotope Measurements in Engineering*. Reinhold.

GUÉRON, J. (1951). *Nucleonics*, **9,** no. 5, 53.

HOFFMANN, A. M. (1960). *Ind. Engng. Chem. Int. Edn.*, **52,** 781.

HOLZHEY, J. (1962). *Isotopentechnik*, **2,** 165.

HOVENKAMP, S. G. (1966). *Int. J. Appl. Radiat. Isotopes*, **19,** 63.

HULL, D. E., and FRIES, B. A. (1956). *Proc. Int. Conf. on Peaceful Uses of Atomic Energy*, **15,** 199, New York.

HULL, D. E., FRIES, B. A., and GILMORE, J. T. (1965). *Int. J. Appl. Radiat. Isotopes*, **16,** 19.

I.A.E.A. Symposium (1961). *Tritium in the Physical and Biological Sciences*. Vienna.

ISRAEL, H., and KREBS, A. (1962). *Nuclear Radiation in Geophysics*. Berlin.

IVES, K. J. (1960). *Int. J. Appl. Radiat. Isotopes*, **9,** 49.

JEFFERSON, S. (1957). *Radioisotopes, a New Tool for Industry*. Newnes.

JEFFERSON, S., and WILDBLOOD, A. M. (1956). *Agric. Merch.*, **74.**

KOHL, J., ZENTNER, R. D., and LUKENS, H. R. (1961). *Radioisotope Applications Engineering*. New York.

LIBBY, W. F. (1961). *J. Geophys. Res.*, **66,** 3767.

SELIGMAN, H. (1954). *Atomics*, **5,** 299.

SCHÜTTE, K. H. (1964). *The Biology of the Trace Elements*. Crosby Lockwood.

VOICE, E. W. (1951a). *Nucleonics*, **9,** no. 10, 13.

VOICE, E. W. (1951b). *J. Iron & Steel Inst.*, **167,** 157.

CHAPTER 3

# Applications in Testing Separation Techniques

Radioactive isotopes offer a valuable tool for the rapid, quantitative evaluation of techniques of radiochemical separation. They have in fact been used in every type of separation technique. Their specificity and ease of detection have saved a great deal of tedious chemical analysis, and in many cases they can be used where conventional methods of analysis have not yet been developed.

Empirical measurements of distribution of a substance between two phases, which are often made by analytical chemists, can also be used to derive physico-chemical data on such quantities as vapour pressures, solubility products, complex-formation constants and $R_f$ values. If these measurements are made over a range of temperatures, the data can be used to calculate heats of solution, adsorption, sublimation and so on. In the majority of cases studied, the analytical requirements have been given more attention than the collection of physico-chemical data, but there is no reason why this should remain so.

The number of separation techniques available to chemists is not very large (Berg, 1963). Some important techniques include the following:

| *Technique* | *Phases* |
|---|---|
| Precipitation | Solid/Liquid |
| Electrodeposition | Solid/Liquid |
| Isotope exchange | Solid/Liquid |
| Ion exchange | Solid/Liquid |
| Chromatography | Solid/Liquid |
| Absorption | Solid/Liquid |
| Solvent extraction | Liquid/Liquid |
| Volatilization | Liquid/Gas |
| Gas chromatography | Solid/Gas |

Many of these techniques have been extensively explored and are the subject of one or more monographs. Here we can only outline how tracers have helped investigations in a few particular instances.

**Precipitation**

Precipitation is a well-established method of separation, though it cannot be said to be well understood (Hermann and Suttle, 1961). In most analytical applications precipitation is carried out rapidly, from supersaturated solutions, leading to considerable occlusion of impurities and solvent molecules in the crystals formed. In homogeneous precipitation (Gordon *et al.*, 1959) the precipitant is generated slowly and uniformly in the solution so that supersaturation is largely avoided, and occlusion is thereby reduced.

An ideal precipitant should be completely specific for the element concerned, and should co-precipitate negligible quantities of other elements from solution. Very few ideal precipitants are known, as the majority of reagents precipitate two or more elements under any given sets of conditions. Example of fairly specific precipitants include:

1M hydrochloric acid treated with $SO_2$, filtered and then treated with KSCN precipitates copper (as CuSCN).

1% Dimethylglyoxime in ethanol precipitates Ni and Pd from M sodium acetate.

80% nitric acid precipitates Ba, Pb, Ra and Sr.

The efficiency of precipitation, and the extent of co-precipitation, is readily measured with tracers. An example is the precipitation of

TABLE 3.1

Co-precipitation of 27 elements with thionalide

| Percentage co-precipitated | |
|---|---|
| >97 | Ag, Au, Hg, In, Ta |
| 50–97 | Hf, Os, Sb, Sn, W |
| 10–50 | Cr, Ir, Ru, Sc, Se, Zr |
| 5–10 | Ce, Fe, Mn, Y, Zn |
| <5 | Co, Cs, Na, Sr, Tl, U |

thionalide from 30% ethanol at pH 3·5 (Lai and Weiss, 1962). Table 3.1 shows the percentage of 27 radioactive elements co-precipitated with the thionalide at this pH. Each of the 27 radio-elements was dissolved in a 15 ml aliquot of 30% ethanol, and 1 ml of 0·5% thionalide in ethanol was added. After the thionalide had precipitated at 0°C it was filtered off, dissolved in ethanol and its count-rate compared with that from an aliquot of the filtrate of similar volume.

Precisely similar methods have been used to assess the efficiency of scavenging precipitates of charged, colloidal substances such as ferric hydroxide (Sunderman and Meinke, 1957; Bowen and Gibbons, 1963). Table 3.2 shows the efficiency of co-precipitation in the presence of carriers.

TABLE 3.2

Efficiency of co-precipitation with ferric hydroxide in presence of carriers

| Percentage co-precipitated | |
|---|---|
| >99·9 | Ce, Nb, La, Zr |
| 99–99·9 | Cr, In |
| 90–99 | Sn |
| 50–90 | Ir, Ru, Sb |
| 10–50 | Co, Se |
| 5–10 | Ag |
| <5 | Cs, I, Sr |

As an example of the determination of solubilities, consider the case of silver chloride. Silver chloride is first precipitated in the presence of $^{110}$Ag; it is washed and dried and its specific activity measured. Suppose this to be $2 \times 10^5$ counts min$^{-1}$ mg$^{-1}$. The precipitate is now shaken with 10 g of water in a constant-temperature bath for about 15 minutes. 1 g aliquots of the solution are transferred to counting trays, dried and counted. If the count-rate is 220 counts min$^{-1}$ g$^{-1}$, the solubility of silver chloride must have been 1·1 mg l$^{-1}$ at the temperature concerned.

## Electrodeposition

Electrodeposition is a special form of precipitation using electrons from a cathode as a reducing agent. It is a relatively slow form of separation, needing at least 30 minutes for complete reduction, and its applicability is limited to those metals which can readily be deposited from aqueous solutions, especially the noble metals such as silver. At least 25 elements can be electrodeposited (Bard, 1966). Unfortunately the method is no more selective than conventional precipitation, as shown by the data in Table 3.3 for electrodeposition of cadmium on a copper cathode (DeVoe and Meinke, 1963).

TABLE 3.3

Selectivity of electrodeposition of cadmium on a copper cathode (conditions; 6 volts; 0·1 amp for 1 hour; electrolyte, 0·2M $HNO_3$)

| Percentage deposited | |
|---|---|
| >99 | Cd, Se |
| >50 | Tl |
| 10–50 | Ag, Ce, Co, Ir, Nb, Ru, Zn |
| 1–10 | Zr |
| <1 | Cs |

## Isotope exchange

An efficient and selective method of separating small amounts of a radioactive isotope from solution involves shaking with an inactive compound of the same element. For example, several metals such as cadmium, indium or zinc can be removed from solution by shaking with a small amount of metal amalgam. The best conditions for

TABLE 3.4

Selectivity of isotopic exchange between aqueous solutions and solid silver chloride

| Percentage exchanged | |
|---|---|
| >99 | Ag |
| 1–10 | Bi, Hg |
| 0·01–0·1 | Ir, Pb, Ru, Se, Sn, Tl |
| 0·001–0·01 | Cr, Sb, Ta, Zr |
| <0·001 | Ba, Ce, Co, Cs, Sr, Y |

isotopic exchange must be determined by experiment, as it may be a slow process.

The specificity of the technique is illustrated by the data in Table 3.4 for the contamination of freshly precipitated silver chloride when shaken with 1M nitric acid containing various radiotracers (Sunderman and Meinke, 1957). This technique is only useful for radiochemical separations.

**Ion exchange**

The technique of ion exchange has been thoroughly reviewed, e.g. by Samuelson (1953), and Walton (1966). The main types of functional groups available in ion exchangers are set out in Table 3.5. The most commonly used ion-exchangers are resin beads made by co-polymerizing derivatives of styrene and divinyl benzene, which are available in various sizes.

TABLE 3.5

Types of synthetic ion exchangers

| Functional group | Ions exchanged | Capacity/ mol kg$^{-1}$ | Examples |
|---|---|---|---|
| —$SO_3^-Na^+$ | Cations | 5 | Amberlite IR-120; Dowex 50; Zeo-Karb 225 |
| —$CO_2H$ | Cations | 10 | Amberlite IRC-50; Zeo-Karb 226 |
| —$NR_3^+Cl^-$ | Anions | 4 | Amberlite IRA-400; De-Acidite FF; Dowex 1; Dowex 2 |

If columns of resin beads are set up, with a simple trap to ensure that they cannot run dry, they can be used

(1) To absorb cations and/or anions from solutions, while allowing neutral molecules to pass through them.
(2) To separate ions of similar charge which, after absorption onto a column, can be eluted off with a suitable eluent solution.

Radioactive tracers are invaluable for determining two empirical parameters when using ion-exchange columns. The *breakthrough volume* is the volume of solution which may be passed through a column before the component of interest appears in the eluate. For example, Bowen (1956) showed that 88% of the barium in 1·5 l of seawater was retained on a 15 cm × 0·75 cm$^2$ column of Zeo-Karb 225, by spiking the seawater with $^{140}$Ba. Secondly, the *elution pattern* of a mixture of ions is highly characteristic. The elution patterns of ions have been thoroughly studied and very many separations have been worked out using tracers. Mother and daughter isotopes can often be separated by ion exchange, e.g. $^{90}$Sr and $^{90}$Y, or $^{132}$Te and $^{132}$I. Especially noteworthy are studies such as those of Strelow *et al.* (1965), who studied the behaviour of 50 elements on cation exchangers over a wide range of pH, and the similar studies of Kraus and Nelson for anion exchangers (1956, 1957). As a result of these studies, automatic ion-exchange separations of up to 23 different elements have now been worked out (Wester *et al.*, 1964; Samsahl, 1966).

### Chromatography

Chromatography is formally similar to ion exchange in that a mixture absorbed onto a solid phase is selectively eluted with a suitable solvent. It is primarily a technique for separating molecules rather than ions, and has an extensive literature (e.g. Lederer and Lederer, 1955; Block, Durrum and Zweig, 1955; Truter, 1962). The commonest solid absorbents used are probably cellulose and silica gel, though many others have been employed. They may be employed as a cylindrical column, a thin layer on a glass plate, or a two-dimensional sheet as in paper chromatography.

Radioactive tracers have been very widely employed to locate substances on columns, thin-layer and paper chromatograms. The chromatogram can be chopped or sliced into a series of segments of equal size, each of which is counted with a suitable detector. Alternatively the undivided chromatogram can be slowly racked across a lead slit shielding the counter, which is coupled to a ratemeter and recorder, so that the distribution of radioactivity is measured automatically. When elution patterns from chromatographic columns are required, an automatic fraction collector can be used to collect successive samples for counting, or the individual drops can be monitored as they build up and fall from the column.

In paper and thin-layer chromatography, the distance moved by a substance divided by the distance moved by the solvent front is a constant, known as the $R_f$ value of the substance. $R_f$ values can readily be determined by using radioactively labelled substances. The main advantages of labelling over other means of detection (such as observation in ultraviolet light, or spraying with colour-reagents) are

(1) Great sensitivity.
(2) Quantitative nature of counting technique.
(3) Some substances neither fluoresce nor give colour reactions, e.g. the organic phosphates studied by Benson *et al.* (1959), which can readily be labelled with phosphorus-32.
(4) The qualitative distribution of radioactivity on a chromatogram can be determined by autoradiography which involves exposing the chromatogram to a photographic film through a thin plastic sheet. This technique may take several days, but gives good resolution when beta-emitters such as carbon-14 are involved (see Chapter 7).

A classical instance of the use of radio-chromatography is the study of photosynthesis (Bassham and Calvin, 1957). If illuminated green leaves or algae are exposed to $^{14}CO_2$ for periods of one second or less, they incorporate radioactivity into several carbohydrate phosphates, but the most strongly labelled compound as the period of exposure is decreased is 3-phosphoglyceric acid. The short exposures are terminated by plunging the tissues into boiling methanol. The labelled compounds are separated by two-dimensional paper chromatography and located by autoradiography.

When chromatography is carried out in a potential gradient it is known as electrophoresis. Electrophoresis is a technique which is widely used for the separation of polar organic molecules (McDonald, 1955; Block *et al.*, 1955; Lederer and Lederer, 1955). A further modification involves electrophoresis of cations in a gradient of complexing agent (Schumacher, 1957). This separates the ions into sharply defined zones in a few minutes, and is known as

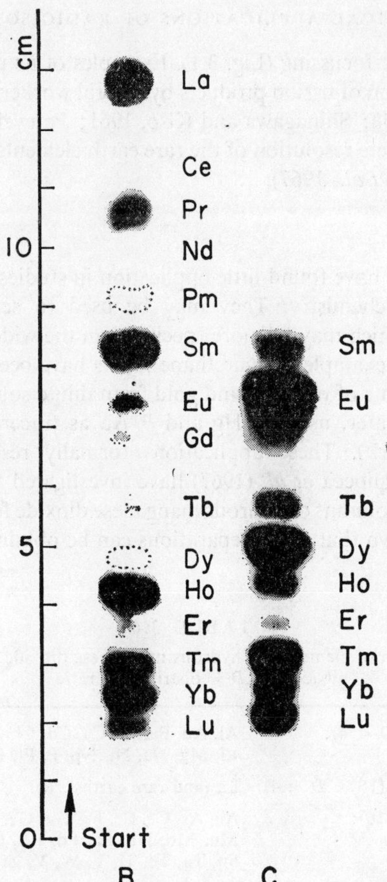


FIG. 3.1. Separation of the lanthanide ions by electrophoretic focussing in 30 minutes. The sample was spotted onto a gelatinized acetylcellulose strip and eluted with 0·8M α-hydroxybutyric acid at 45 V $cm^{-1}$. Detection by autoradiography. B = separation of radioactive lanthanides; C = inactive lanthanides separated and activated by thermal neutrons after separation. (After Aitzetmüller *et al.*, 1967)

electrophoretic focussing (Fig. 3.1). Examples of its use include the rapid separation of fission products by several workers (Schumacher and Streif, 1958; Shinagawa and Kiso, 1961; Pauwels *et al.*, 1966), and the complete resolution of the rare earth elements in 15 minutes (Aitzetmüller *et al.*, 1967).

### Absorption

Radioisotopes have found little application in studies of absorption in analytical chemistry. They may be used to screen potential absorbents, which may be more specific than the widely used active charcoal. For example, polyurethane foams have been shown to be good absorbents of mercury and gold from dilute solutions of these elements in water, using $^{203}$Hg and $^{198}$Au as tracers (Bowen, unpublished work). These applications formally resemble solvent extraction. Bigliocca *et al.* (1967) have investigated the absorption behaviour of columns of hydrous manganese dioxide for 61 elements, and have shown that many separations can be obtained in this way (Table 3.6).

TABLE 3.6

Absorption of elements by hydrous manganese dioxide from 0·1M nitric acid; $D$ = distribution ratio

| | |
|---|---|
| Not absorbed ($D < 4$): | Al, Au, Ba, Br, Ca, Cd, Cl, Co, Cs, Cu, F, Ir, Li, Mg, Na, Ni, Np, P, Pt, Re, Sr, Tc, U, Zn |
| Partly absorbed ($16 > D > 4$): | La (and rare earths), Ru |
| Absorbed ($D > 16$): | Ag, As, Ce, Cr, Fe, Ga, Ge, Hf, Hg, I, In, K, Mn, Mo, Nb, Pa, Pd, Rb, Os, S, Sb, Sc, Se, Sn, Ta, Te, Ti, V, W, Y, Zr |

### Liquid–liquid extraction

The partition of a solute between two immiscible solvents has been of practical importance for many years, but three developments have been outstanding in the last few decades.

(1) The use of radionuclides to measure percentage extraction, and hence distribution ratios.

(2) The use of organic complexing agents as ligands.
(3) Comprehensive theory.

The use of radionuclides may be illustrated by the simple case of the partition of iodine between water and carbon tetrachloride. The small amount of iodine soluble in water is very largely extracted by shaking with an equal volume of carbon tetrachloride, and the analysis of the minute amount remaining presents problems. However, if the iodine is labelled with $^{131}$I, the iodine in both layers can readily be determined by counting, and the distribution ratio is

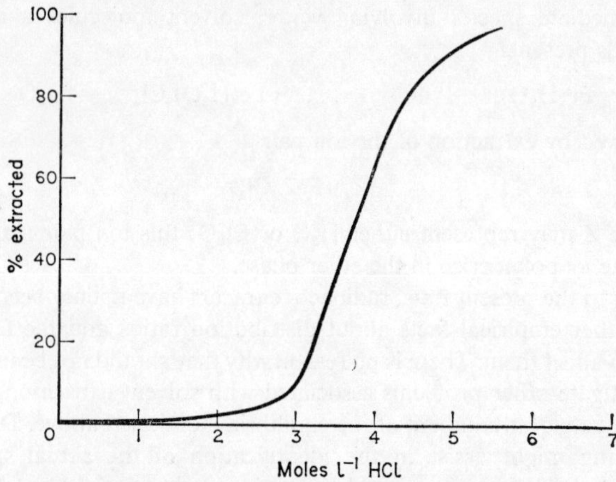


FIG. 3.2. Percentage extraction of $^{59}$Fe(III) from hydrochloric acid into diethyl ether

simply the ratio of counts sec$^{-1}$ for the two solvents. It is also an easy matter to establish the time needed to reach equilibrium, or the minimum shaking period. This may be a matter of seconds, as in the case of iodine, or a matter of hours, as with some metallic dithizonates (McClellan and Freiser, 1964). The effects of varying such quantities as pH, temperature and ionic strength are readily studied by the tracer method.

According to the Nernst theory of extraction, the thermodynamic activity of any species in one solvent should bear a constant ratio to the thermodynamic activity in the other, provided equilibrium has been reached at a given temperature. This constant is called the partition coefficient, and is not the same as the measured distribution ratio. Many cases are known where distribution ratios are far from constant. For example, Morrison and Freiser (1957) state that the distribution ratio of radio-iron(III) between 6M hydrochloric acid and diethyl ether is only constant at concentrations below $10^{-4}$M. At higher concentrations the distribution ratio increases with increasing concentration of iron(III) (Fig. 3.2). The observations have been satisfactorily interpreted in terms of stepwise formation of intermediate species involving water, solvent molecules and any ligands present:

$$Fe(H_2O)_6{}^{3+} + 4Cl^- \rightleftharpoons \ldots \rightleftharpoons Fe(H_2O)_2Cl_4{}^- + 4H_2O$$

followed by extraction of the ion pair

$$HZ^+ \; FeZ_2Cl_4{}^-$$

where Z may represent either $H_2O$ or $Et_2O$: this ion pair may dissociate or polymerize in the ether phase.

Up to the present time, radioactive tracers have mainly been used to gather empirical facts about distribution ratios and the factors which affect them. There is no reason why they should not be used to investigate other problems associated with solvent extraction, such as the rate of attainment of the equilibria mentioned above. Double labelling might assist in the identification of the actual species extracted. Thus the ion complex mentioned above could be labelled with both $^{59}Fe$ and $^{36}Cl$, of known specific activities, to determine its chemical formula.

**Volatilization**

Volatilization is an attractive method of separation which is both rapid and selective. It is widely used for separating organic compounds, but is less widely applicable to inorganic compounds because of their high boiling points. Nevertheless, it is often used to separate inorganic molecular substances such as the halogens, non-metal hydrides, mercury, ruthenium(VIII) and osmium(VIII) oxides, chromyl chloride, permanganic acid, etc. Radioactive tracers have been widely employed to test the percentages volatilized and condensed, and to evaluate the contamination involved.

One of the simplest and best known volatilizations is that of carbon dioxide, which can be quantitatively boiled out of aqueous solutions and absorbed in alkali. This process has been intensively studied in view of its importance in the radiochemical purification of the $^{14}CO_2$ used for carbon-14 dating. The volatilization step frees the radiocarbon from all radioactive impurities other than certain gases, which include $^{85}Kr$, $^{222}Rn$ and $T_2O$. The latter is removed by drying, while the inert gases can be selectively absorbed into active charcoal or boiled out of the absorbent solution (Libby, 1955).

Many ingenious separations have been made by rapid volatilization of short-lived radionuclides (Kusaka and Meinke, 1961). For example 0·53 second $^{73m}Ge$ was distilled in a stream of nitrogen + chlorine from a solution containing 76 day $^{73}As$ in 12M hydrochloric acid. The chlorine served to keep the arsenic parent in the involatile pentavalent state (Campbell and Nelson, 1957). 15·5 second $^{88}Br$ and 1·6 second $^{90}Br$ were distilled from fission products (i.e. neutron-irradiated $^{235}U$ in solution in 1M nitric acid and 0·5M potassium bromate), and absorbed by carbon tetrachloride. The distillation was carried out in a current of air containing about 0·2% bromine carrier. The bromate served both to oxidize bromide ions to bromine, and to oxidize any fission product iodine to involatile iodate (Perlow and Stehney, 1957).

The volatilization of metals in a vacuum has been studied using tracer techniques. The following metals boil at less than 1000°C: Hg (366); As (615); Cs (670); Se (688); Rb (700); K (760); Cd (767); Na (892); Zn (907). In a high vacuum, mercury can be distilled at 100°C, and cadmium at 180°C, at a rate of about 0·2 mg $min^{-1}$, but the decontamination from other metals is not outstandingly good (DeVoe and Meinke, 1963). It is also possible to measure the vapour pressures of metals and other involatile materials by tracer methods (Nesmeyanov, 1958). Three techniques have been suggested. In the first, or *static technique* a labelled solid, such as $^{32}P_2O_5$, is equilibrated with an evacuated vessel at a suitable temperature. The solid is then removed, and the radioactivity of a known volume of vapour is measured. The *Langmuir technique* uses measurements of the mass $m$ kg of a substance which volatilizes from a sample of cross-sectional area $A$ m$^2$ in $t$ seconds. The vapour pressure $p$ at temperature $T$ is given by

$$p = \frac{m}{At}\sqrt{\left(\frac{2\pi RT}{M}\right)} \text{ N m}^{-2}$$

where $M$ is the molecular weight in u and $R$ is the gas constant, 8·314 J K$^{-1}$ mol$^{-1}$. Unweighably small masses of substances with a high specific activity can be measured from their radioactivity. Thus the vapour pressure of $^{89}$SrO on a platinum filament was measured from the amount of activity volatilized from a 1 curie source. In the *isotope exchange technique*, two metal discs which are identical apart from one being highly radioactive, are placed near one another (but not touching) *in vacuo* at a suitable temperature. Radioactivity is slowly transferred from one disc to the other, and the rate of transfer is a complicated function of vapour pressure.

With 1 curie of radioactivity, each of these techniques is able to measure vapour pressures down to 10$^{-15}$ bar (10$^{-10}$ N m$^{-2}$).

Another valuable application of radionuclides is in the measurement of losses by volatilization during the ashing of biological material prior to inorganic analysis. In a systematic study of 14 elements, Gorsuch (1959) found several to be volatile during ashing (allowance was made for retention of some elements by the crucible). In addition many non-metals, such as carbon, nitrogen, sulphur and the halogens, may be wholly or partly volatilized on ashing together with Re, Ru and Os; and in the presence of strong hydrochloric acid As, Ge, Sb, Se, Sn, Te, may be volatilized (Table 3.7). More than 50% of the tracer $^{203}$Hg may be lost by prolonged storage of aqueous solutions at 60°C (Brune, 1966).

Elements may also be lost when solids are heated. For example, Weinstein *et al.* (1957) showed that impurities such as Bi, Ce, K, Mo, Na and Zr in uranium oxide and other oxide matrices, could be removed by volatilization below the melting point. The minimum temperature for volatilization was about $0{\cdot}55T_{\text{melting}}$, or close to the Tammann temperature of the solid, and was not related to the impurity atom. Nickel (1965) labelled graphite anodes with $^{59}$Fe and showed that iron distilled across to the cathode in a d.c. arc.

Tracer methods have not been widely used in investigating the powerful technique of gas chromatography. Current detection techniques are capable of determining $10^{-12}$ g of some unlabelled organic substances (Purnell, 1962) so there is seldom a demand for the still higher sensitivity attainable for labelled substances of high specific activity. The residence-time of the eluate in the counter used

TABLE 3.7

Volatility of elements during heating or ashing

| Type of ashing | Temp. /°C | Elements partly volatilized | Elements not volatilized | Reference |
|---|---|---|---|---|
| Warming | 60 | As, Br, Cl, Hg, I, N | Most other | Brune, 1966; Satterlee and Blodgett, 1944 |
| W t($HNO_3$/ $HClO_4$) | 200 | Br, Cl, F, Hg, I, N, Os, Ru, S, Se | Ag, As, Cd, Co, Cr, Cu, Fe, Pb, Sb, Sr, Mo, Zn, etc. | Gorsuch, 1959 |
| Molten $NaNO_3$/ $KNO_3$ | ~400 | Br, Cl, Hg, I, N, S, Se | Ag, As, Au, Cd, Ce, Co, Cr, Cs, Cu, Fe, Ir, Mn, Mo, Na, Re, Ru, Sb, Sr, Tl, Zn | Bowen, 1968 |
| Heating in air | 450–550 | Ag, As, Au, Br, Cd, Cl, Fe, Hg, I, Os, Pb, Ru, Se | Co, Cr, Cu, Mo, Na, Sb, Sr, Zn | Gorsuch, 1959; Gleit and Holland, 1962 |
| Radio-frequency/ $O_2$ | 100 | Ag, Au, Hg, I | As, Co, Cr, Cs, Au, Fe, Mn, Mo, Na, Pb, Sb, Se, Zn | Gleit and Holland, 1962 |

to detect radioactivity is critical in this respect (Wolfgang and Rowland, 1958). The separation and determination of alkanes labelled with $^{14}C$ or $^{3}H$, and of alkyl halides labelled with $^{38}Cl$, $^{80}Br$, $^{82}Br$ or $^{128}I$ have been studied by several workers (e.g. Evans and Willard, 1956; Gordus and Willard, 1957; Riesz and Wilzbach, 1958). According to Wolfgang and Rowland, the limit of detectability is 2 dis $sec^{-1}$ and in practice $10^{-15}$ g $CH_3{}^{80}Br$ is readily assayed (Evans and Willard, 1956).

## References


AITZETMÜLLER, K., BUCHTELA, K., and GRASS, F. (1967). *Analytica Chim. Acta*, **38,** 249.

BARD, A. J. (1966). *Analyt. Chem.*, **38,** 88R.

BASSHAM, J. A., and CALVIN, M. (1957). *The Path of Carbon in Photosynthesis*. Prentice Hall.

BENSON, A. A., MARUO, B., FLIPSE, R. J., YUROW, H. W., and MILLER, W. W. (1959). *Proc. Int. Conf. on Peaceful Uses of Atomic Energy*, **24,** 289, New York.

BERG, E. W. (1963). *Physical and Chemical Methods of Separation*. McGraw-Hill.

BIGLIOCCA, C., GIRARDI, F., PAULY, J., SABBIONI, E., MELONI, S., and PROVASOLI, A. (1967). *Analyt. Chem.*, **39,** 1634.

BLOCK, R. J., DURRUM, E. L., and ZWEIG, G. (1955). *A Manual of Paper Chromatography and Electrophoresis*. Academic Press.

BOWEN, H. J. M. (1956). *J. Mar. Biol. Ass. U.K.*, **35,** 451.

BOWEN, H. J. M. (1968). *Analyt. Chem.*, **40,** 969.

BOWEN, H. J. M., and GIBBONS, D. (1963). *Radioactivation Analysis*. Oxford University Press.

BRUNE, D. (1966). *Report AE*-**213**. Aktiebolaget Atomenergi, Stockholm, Sweden.

CAMPBELL, E. C., and NELSON, F. (1957). *Phys. Rev.*, **107,** 502.

DE VOE, J. R., and MEINKE, W. W. (1963). *Analyt. Chem.*, **35,** 2.

EVANS, J. B., and WILLARD, J. E. (1956). *J. Am. Chem. Soc.*, **78,** 2908.

FREISER, H. (1966). *Analyt. Chem.*, **38,** 131R.

GLEIT, C. E., and HOLLAND, W. W. (1962). *Analyt. Chem.*, **34,** 1454.

GORDON, L., SALUTSKY, M. L., and WILLARD, H. H. (1959). *Precipitation from Homogeneous Solution*. Wiley.

GORDUS, A. A., and WILLARD, J. E. (1957). *J. Am. Chem. Soc.*, **79,** 4609.

GORSUCH, T. T. (1959). *Analyst, Lond.*, **84,** 135.

HERMANN, J. A., and SUTTLE, J. F. (1961). *Treatise on Analytical Chemistry*, edited by Kolthoff, I. M., Elving, P. J., and Sandell, E. B., 3, 1367. Interscience.

KRAUS, K. A., and NELSON, F. (1956). *Am. Soc. Testing Mater. Special Tech. Publicn.*, **195,** 27.

KRAUS, K. A., and NELSON, F. (1957). *A. Rev. Nucl. Sci.*, **7,** 31.

KUSAKA, Y., and MEINKE, W. W. (1961). Report NAS-NS 3104. Office of Technical Services, Washington D.C.

LAI, M. G., and WEISS, H. V. (1962). *Analyt. Chem.*, **34,** 1012.

LEDERER, M., and LEDERER, E. (1955). *Chromatography*. Elsevier.

LIBBY, W. F. (1955). *Radiocarbon Dating*. Oxford University Press.

MARCUS, Y. (1963). *Chem. Rev.*, **63,** 139.

MCCLELLAN, B. E., and FREISER, H. (1964). *Analyt. Chem.*, **36,** 2263.

McDONALD, H. J. (1955). *Ionography and Electrophoresis in Stabilized Media*. Chicago University Press.

MORRISON, G. H., and FREISER, H. (1957). *Solvent Extraction in Analytical Chemistry*. Wiley.

NESMEYANOV, H. (1958). *Int. J. Appl. Radiat. Isotopes*, **4,** 16.

NICKEL, H. (1965). *Z. Analyt. Chem.*, **209,** 243.

PAUWELS, M., GIJBELS, R., and HOSTE, J. (1966). *Analytica Chim. Acta*, **36,** 210.

PERLOW, G. J., and STEHNEY, A. F. (1957). *Phys. Rev.*, **107,** 776.

PURNELL, H. (1962). *Gas Chromatography*. Wiley.

RIESZ, P., and WILZBACH, K. E. (1958). *J. Phys. Chem.*, **62,** 6.

SAMSAHL, K. (1966). *Repts AE-***215** *and AE-***247.** Aktiebolaget Atomenergi, Stockholm, Sweden.

SAMUELSON, O. (1953). *Ion Exchangers in Analytical Chemistry*. Wiley.

SATTERLEE, H. S., and BLODGETT, G. (1944). *Ind. Engng. Chem. Analyt. Edn.*, **16,** 400.

SCHUMACHER, E. (1957). *Helv. Chim. Acta*, **40,** 221 and 2322.

SHINAGAWA, M., and KISO, Y. (1961). *Japan Analyst*, **10,** 912.

STRELOW, F. W. E., RETHEMEYER, R., and BOTHMA, C. J. C. (1965). *Analyt. Chem.*, **37,** 106.

SUNDERMAN, D. N., and MEINKE, W. W. (1957). *Analyt. Chem.*, **29,** 1578.

TADMOR, J. (1961). *J. Inorg. Nucl. Chem.*, **23,** 158.

TADMOR, J. (1964). *Analyt. Chem.*, **36,** 1565.

TRUTER, E. V. (1962). *Thin-film Chromatography*. Cleaver-Hume.

WALTON, H. F. (1966). *Analyt. Chem.*, **38,** 79R.

WEINSTEIN, E. E., PAVLENKO, L. I., and BELYAEV, Y. I. (1957). *Int. J. Appl. Radiat. Isotopes*, **2,** 196.

WESTER, P. O., BRUNE, D., and SAMSAHL, K. (1964). *Int. J. Appl. Radiat. Isotopes*, **15,** 59.

## CHAPTER 4

# Applications in Chemical Analysis

**Radiometric techniques**

In radiometric techniques, the unknown substance Q which is to be determined is made to react quantitatively with a radioactive reagent R* of known specific activity, $s$ counts $s^{-1}$ $mol^{-1}$. The excess reagent is removed and the activity ($a$ counts $s^{-1}$) of a radioactive product such as R*Q is determined. The number of moles of the unknown substance Q is given by $a/s$, assuming that R* and Q react in a one-to-one molar ratio.

The advantages of such techniques include:

(1) Wide applicability, even for unknowns without suitable radiotracers.

(2) Sensitivity which may extend from milligram down to nanogram levels, or theoretically even lower.

(3) Good precision which depends on the time available for counting.

(4) The product R*Q need not be chemically pure, provided all excess of R* has been removed.

The main disadvantages are the following:

(1) Poor selectivity. If substances other than Q in the sample react with R*, they must be separated before or after the reaction, or they will interfere.

(2) The need for a quantitative separation of the radioactive product; this can be eliminated by combining the technique with isotope dilution.

(3) The reagent R* must be radiochemically pure. At high specific activities R* may be subject to radiolytic oxidation or decomposition.

Several different radiometric techniques are discussed below.

**Precipitation with a radioreagent**

In its original form, this technique was used to determine substances which can be quantitatively precipitated from solution. For example, chlorides, bromides and iodides may be precipitated using silver labelled with $^{110}Ag$; alternatively silver may itself be determined by precipitation with Na $^{131}I$. Again sulphates or chromates may be precipitated using $^{131}Ba$ or $^{212}Pb$, or the analysis may be reversed, as in the determination of barium or lead in solution by precipitation with sulphuric acid-S35. Practical detection limits are about 0·5 mg $l^{-1}$ of the halogens and 37 mg $l^{-1}$ for barium (Scott and Driscoll, 1961). Other examples of radioactive reagents include phosphoric acid-P32 as a precipitant for Al, Be, Bi, Ga, In, Th, U, Zr and the lanthanides; sodium cobaltinitrite-Co60 for potassium; calcium chloride-Ca45 for fluoride (sensitivity 50 mg $l^{-1}$); and potassium tungstate-W185 for precipitating 1–10 $\mu$g proteins (Shefner *et al.*, 1957). However, few, if any, of these techniques are used routinely and it is worth considering why this is so. There seem to be two reasons:

(a) The radiometric technique is no more selective, and scarcely more sensitive, than other techniques such as spectrophotometry or microgravimetry.

(b) The potential sensitivity of radiometric methods cannot be reached in many cases where substances present in low concentrations fail to precipitate. For example, the solubility of potassium cobaltinitrite is 900 mg $l^{-1}$ at 0°C. Hence one cannot determine smaller concentrations of potassium than about 7 $\mu$mol $ml^{-1}$ by precipitation, even by using sodium cobaltinitrite-Co60 with a specific activity of 15 mCi $\mu mol^{-1}$, which is readily available.

**Dissolution of radioactive solids**

Several techniques have recently been evolved for measuring very low concentrations of substances in water by making these substances react quantitatively with a radioactive solid, and measuring the increase in activity in the solution. Of outstanding interest is the determination of dissolved oxygen in water utilizing its reaction with thallium metal labelled with thallium-204 (Richter and Gillespie, 1962). The reaction is

$$4Tl(s) + O_2 + 2H_2O \longrightarrow 4Tl^+ + 4OH^-$$

so that 1 $\mu$g $O_2$ liberates 25·6 $\mu$g thallous ion into solution. In practice, a water sample was passed through a column containing $^{204}Tl$ electroplated onto copper or molybdenum turnings. With a specific activity of 2 mCi $g^{-1}$ it was possible to determine 0·2 mg $l^{-1}$, and since specific activities of at least 2 Ci $g^{-1}$ are available the limit of detection may be less than 0·2 ng $ml^{-1}$ of oxygen. The true limit will be determined by the solubility of metallic thallium in water, which has not been measured. Other oxidants, such as ozone, fluorine and chlorine, interfered with the determination. Dissolved salts did not interfere, but gave rise to a non-linear calibration curve if metallic copper was used as a support for the thallium.

In the same way, concentrations of dichromate ion in water down to 10 ng $ml^{-1}$ can be measured by acidifying the solution with sulphuric acid and treating with metallic silver labelled with silver-110. The reaction is

$$6Ag(s) + Cr_2O_7^{2-} + 14H^+ \longrightarrow 6Ag^+ + 2Cr^{3+} + 7H_2O.$$

Chloride ion could interfere by precipitating silver chloride, so before measuring the activity of the solution it was made alkaline with ammonia to dissolve any silver chloride formed (Richter and Gillespie, 1965).

**Radioreagents in chromatography and functional group analysis**

Radioactive reagents can be used to develop paper chromatograms in the same manner as can inactive colour reagents. If the excess reagent can be washed off, the technique can be made quantitative. An early example was the determination of heavy metal ions on filter paper by exposure to hydrogen sulphide-S35 (Van Erkelens, 1953). Excess of the gaseous reagent is readily removed, and the activity of the labelled sulphides can be determined by counting or by autoradiography. This technique has been more widely used in organic chemistry. For example, unsaturated fatty acids, such as linoleic acid, will react with iodine vapour, labelled with $^{131}I$, applied to the chromatogram. Excess iodine is easily volatilized. Saturated fatty acids on chromatograms may be converted to their silver salts, excess silver removed, and then reacted with sodium iodide-I 131. Specific radioreagents for certain functional groups are coming into use. For example, alcohols, amines and carboxylic acids may be acetylated using acetic anhydride-C14, or labelled with *p*-iodobenzoyl chloride-I 131. Apart from chromatographic detection and determination, these functional group analyses may be used to characterize unknown compounds present in microgram amounts on chromatograms. At present milligram quantities are required for conventional analyses of active hydrogen by the Zerewitinov method (Overton, 1963) but microgram quantities may be determined using lithium aluminium tritide (Seaman and Stewart, 1964). Other radioreagent modifications of current techniques, such as tritiation or iodination of carbon–carbon double bonds, have not been as fully exploited as they could be in ultramicroanalysis.

The quantitative reaction of the aldehyde group with sodium cyanide-C14 has been used for determining both reducing sugars and end-groups in polysaccharides (Moyer and Isbell, 1958). The comparative sensitivity of physical, chemical and radioreagent techniques in organic analysis is given in Table 4.1.

TABLE 4.1
Techniques for analysis of functional groups

| Technique | Mass of substance required | Ref. |
|---|---|---|
| Infrared spectrometry | 1–10 mg | Schwarz, 1964 |
| Ultraviolet spectrometry | 0·1–10 mg | ,, |
| Nuclear magnetic resonance spectrometry | 5–100 mg | ,, |
| Mass spectrometry | 0·01–1 mg | ,, |
| Chemical analysis | 1–10 mg | Overton, 1963 |
| Radioreagent analysis using | | |
| $^{14}C$ | 20 ng | assuming $10^{-8}$ Ci |
| $^{35}S$ | 1 ng | needed for |
| $^{131}I$ or $^{3}H$ | 50 pg | counting* |

* Cramer *et al.* (1966) claim to be able to measure $10^{-11}$ Ci of carbon-14 after gas chromatography.

**Radioreagents liberating radioactive gases**

A variety of reagents have been suggested for this modification of the radioreagent method. For example, Wallace and Willard (1950) determined the water content of organic solvents by measuring the $H^{36}Cl$ liberated from aluminium chloride-Cl36. A more sensitive reaction, using 0·2M lithium aluminium hydride-H3 in pentanol-3 as a radioreagent, and measuring the tritium evolved, has been described by Chleck *et al.* (1960). This reagent is non-specific, as it reacts not only with water but with 'active' hydrogen from alcohols, amino compounds, etc. Hence it can be used for determining 'active' hydrogen in pure compounds. Yet another reagent for determining water in organic solvents is solid calcium carbide-Kr85. When the carbide dissolves in water, gaseous krypton-85 is liberated and can be carried off in a stream of nitrogen for counting (Chleck *et al.*, 1965).

Solids labelled with krypton-85 have been suggested as 'universal reagents' by Chleck and co-workers (1963). Among their many applications, their use in gas analysis is perhaps the most promising. For example, from $10^{-5}$ to $10^{5}$ p.p.m. of oxygen can be determined in gas samples as follows. The gas is passed over a small piece of copper foil labelled with $^{85}Kr$, maintained at some temperature between 500° and 1000°C. The rate of loss of $^{85}Kr$ as the copper surface is oxidized can be followed with a Geiger counter. Similar techniques have been applied to measure ozone (kryptonated copper at 200°C), hydrogen (kryptonated $PtO_2$ at 0°–300°C), fluorine and reactive gaseous fluorides. As little as 1 part in $10^{10}$ by volume of sulphur dioxide in air can be determined by passing the air sample through acidified potassium iodate-I 131 solution and measuring the iodine liberated by the reaction:

$$2H^{131}IO_3 + 5SO_2 + 4H_2O \longrightarrow {}^{131}I_2 + 5H_2SO_4$$

Hydrogen sulphide and other reducing agents in the air stream may interfere (Ross and Lyon, 1965).

Free radicals in the gas phase are readily determined by radioreagent techniques. In early work, methyl radicals were determined by their reaction with metallic mirrors containing $^{212}Pb$ or $^{210}Bi$, forming volatile methyl derivatives. This technique has been superseded by the reaction of the radicals with $^{131}I_2$ in the gas phase. Although alkanes do not react readily with gaseous iodine, free alkyl radicals do so, and the radioactive iodides produced can be trapped and separated by gas chromatography. In this way it is possible to determine the proportions of methyl, ethyl, and other radicals in complex mixtures (Holroyd and Klein, 1962).

**Radiometric titrations**

In radiometric titrations, one titrates the unknown substance with a radioreagent and measures the activity of a readily separable phase. Alternatively one can use a radioactive indicator which liberates its radioactivity when the end-point is reached. The techniques have been largely worked out by Russian and Hungarian workers (Mikheyeva and Mikheyev, 1961; Alimarin *et al.*, 1957; Braun *et al.*, 1964). They give sharp end-points and can be used to

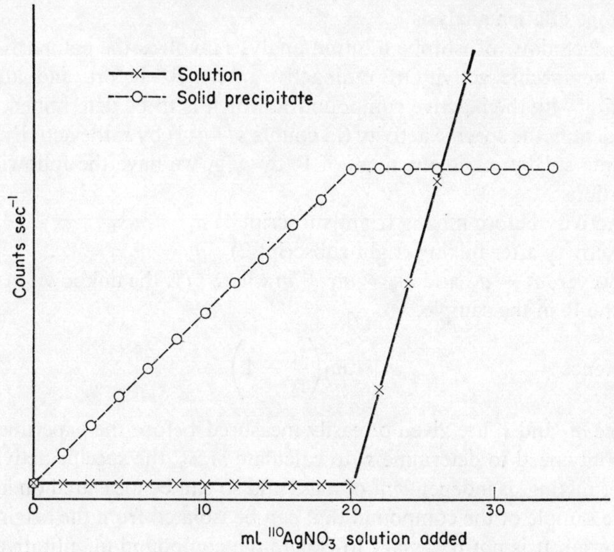


FIG. 4.1. Radiometric titration of $^{110}AgNO_3$ with NaCl

detect microgram amounts of substances where milligram amounts would be required for conventional volumetric analysis. An example is the titration of metals which form insoluble phosphates, such as Al, Be, Mg, Pb, Th, U and Zr, with sodium phosphate-P32, and measuring the activity of the solution after each addition. Similar titrations have been carried out with Co, Cu and Zn by running in potassium ferrocyanide-Fe59 (Fig. 4.1). Duncan and Thomas (1957) titrated $^{60}Co$ and $^{203}Hg$ in aqueous solution with dithizone in carbon tetrachloride, and measured the activity remaining in the aqueous phase after each addition. Many radioactive indicators have been suggested, and a good example is metallic zinc labelled with krypton-85. This has been used to find the end-point both when titrating strong acids into solutions of alkalies, and for titrating thorium nitrate (pH 3·4) into solutions of fluorides (Maehl *et al.*, 1965).

## Isotope dilution analysis

The technique of isotope dilution analysis involves the comparison of the specific activity of radioactive tracer R* before and after mixing with the inactive compound R which is to be determined. If we denote the specific activity (in counts $s^{-1}$ $g^{-1}$) by $s$, the activity in counts $s^{-1}$ by $a$ and the mass of R by $m$ g, we have the following relations:

Activity before mixing (right subscript 1) $a_1 = m_1 s_1$

Activity after mixing (right subscript 2) $a_2 = m_2 s_2$

However, $a_1 = a_2$, and $m_2 = m_1 + m$ where $m$ is the unknown mass of the R in the sample.

Hence
$$m = m_1\left(\frac{s_1}{s_2} - 1\right)$$

Since $m_1$ and $s_1$ are given or easily measured before the experiment we only need to determine $s_2$ to calculate $m$. $s_2$, the specific activity after mixing, is independent of mass and so can be measured on any pure sample of the compound that can be isolated from the original material. It is not necessary to isolate the compound quantitatively provided that the final sample obtained is pure.

The advantages of the isotope dilution technique are the following:

(1) It has a wide range of application, from the analysis of individual elements to the determination of large molecules.
(2) It has a high sensitivity, sometimes extending to submicrogram levels, which is usually limited either by the mass needed to effect a separation, or by the technique used to measure $m_2$.
(3) It is highly selective, e.g. it can be used to determine $\gamma$-benzene hexachloride in a mixture of isomers.
(4) It is capable of high precision, since the precision is equal to the square root of the total number of counts recorded. Thus for $10^6$ counts, the precision would be $10^3$ counts or 0·1%.
(5) The chemical separation steps need not be quantitative.
(6) It can be used for unstable substances which partially decompose during their isolation, provided that a pure sample is ultimately obtained for weighing and counting.

On the other hand there are certain difficulties in applying the technique, among which the following are prominent:

(1) There are no suitable radioisotopes for labelling atoms of boron, lithium, nitrogen and oxygen (nor for helium and neon).
(2) Labelled tracer molecules are often difficult or even impossible to make, and may therefore be expensive or not available. For example, it is not possible to make proteins labelled in specific ways, nor high-polymer molecules of a single chain-length.
(3) The tracer used must be radiochemically pure, which is sometimes difficult to ensure because of radiation-sensitized decomposition.
(4) The method fails if the tracer is not thoroughly mixed and equilibrated with the sample, which may present problems.
(5) The compound isolated after mixing must be chemically and radiochemically pure.
(6) Like most other analytical techniques, the method can be vitiated by reagents contaminated with the substance to be isolated. Blanks should therefore be run.

The first application of isotope dilution was the determination of lead in amounts down to 1 $\mu$g in minerals (Hevesey and Hobbie,

1932). Since that time it has been used for a very wide variety of analyses, e.g. determination of hydrogen in metals, using tritium (Evans and Herrington, 1962), determination of metals such as cobalt, vanadium and molybdenum in steel, and especially in organic analysis (Sorensen, 1957) where it has been used to determine particular fatty acids or amino-acids in mixtures, substituted phenoxyacetic acids in herbicides, and complex mixtures of sterols, nucleotides, phosphatides or penicillins. It is in fact especially useful when determining a substance in the presence of a large number of closely analogous materials. Full details of a student experiment on the determination of cobalt are given below to illustrate an actual example.

**Determination of cobalt in a complex salt**

The complex salt provided is Aquo pentammine cobalt(III) chloride, $[CoH_2O(NH_3)_5]Cl_3$. A 100 mg sample of the salt is weighed out into a centrifuge tube, and to it is added a weighed drop of a solution of cobalt chloride-Co60, containing 0·3 mg Co per g. A second radioactive drop is weighed onto an aluminium counting tray, dried, and counted to obtain the specific activity. The salt is decomposed by boiling with 5 ml 20% potassium hydroxide, and the cobalt hydroxide is spun down and drained. The precipitate is treated with 2 ml hot glacial acetic acid plus a few drops of hydrogen peroxide until a clear pink solution is obtained. This is diluted with an equal volume of water and 1 g of solid potassium nitrite is added. The yellow precipitate of potassium cobaltinitrite is spun down, washed and transferred to a counting tray (this need not be quantitative). By combining the count rates from the cobalt chloride-Co60 standard and the cobaltinitrite precipitate with the measured weights, the mass of cobalt in the original salt may be calculated. In a typical experiment the percentages of cobalt found were 21·96, 22·57, 20·52, 21·05: mean 21·53, theoretical 21·95.

Several recent modifications of isotope dilution analysis are described below.

**Reverse isotope dilution**

This is a technique for measuring small amounts of a radioactive substance R* dispersed in a large volume of inactive sample. It can only be applied when the original specific activity $s_1$ of the radioactive label is known. The technique involves addition of a known mass $m$ of inactive carrier R, homogenization, and isolation of a pure sample of R*R for determination of its specific activity $s_2$. The isolation need not be quantitative, and the mass $m_1$ of radioactive material present is given by

$$m_1 = \frac{ms_2}{s_1 - s_2}$$

It has been used, for example, to determine the amounts of radioactive vitamin $B_{12}$ deposited in various mammalian organs after administration. Currie *et al.*, (1965) have used radioactive cerium-139 to carry out 'radioisotope dilution analysis' of cerium-144.

**Substoichiometric isotope dilution**

This is based on the principle of separating equal masses of the substance R from both the isotopically diluted sample and the original radioactive tracer R*. In order to do this, it is sufficient to add to each solution equal amounts of some reagent S which reacts quantitatively with R so that the product RS is readily separable. It is usual to add substoichiometric amounts of the reagent S, that is, amounts less than those required to react with all the R present.

Then

$$m = m_1\left(\frac{a_1}{a_2} - 1\right)$$

using the notation of p. 50 with specific activities replaced by relative activities (Ruzicka and Stary, 1964). Suitable reagents include chelating agents such as cupferron for iron, dithizone for Ag, Cu, Hg and Zn, and EDTA for iron and lanthanides.

Ruzicka and Williams (1965) have suggested that this technique could readily be automated. A peristaltic pump may be used to circulate metered quantities of R, R* and S through a continuously flowing system monitored by a Geiger or scintillation counter. Separations may be carried out automatically by ion exchange or by solvent extraction, but it is difficult to automate separations involving a precipitation step.

**Saturation analysis or immuno-assay**

This is a very sensitive method of analysis, used especially for proteins which possess specific binding agents or antibodies. Here it is subject to the difficulty of labelling proteins without modifying their behaviour, which has not been completely overcome. A known mass $m^*$ labelled protein P* is allowed to react with a substoichiometric amount of antibody A: the complex P*A is isolated and counted. At the same time and under identical conditions, an identical mass $m^*$ of P* is mixed with an unknown mass $m$ of inactive protein P, allowed to react with the same amount of antibody A as before, and the complex PP*A is isolated and counted. If the activities of the complexes are $a^*$ and $a$, it is easy to show that

$$m = m^*\left(\frac{a^*}{a} - 1\right)$$

In an actual example (Hales and Randle, 1963), insulin was iodinated using iodine monochloride-I 131 and the product, purified by dialysis, could be obtained with a specific activity in the range 5–20 Ci $g^{-1}$. 0·25 ng aliquots of labelled insulin, with or without unknown amounts of inactive insulin, were then incubated with insulin antibody at 4°C for 4 hours. The insulin–antibody complexes were then precipitated by incubation with anti $\gamma$-globulin serum overnight, and the precipitates were collected on millipore filters, washed and counted. In this way it was possible to determine amounts of insulin down to 0·25 ng.

**Combined radiometric and isotope dilution analyses**

The determination of amino-acids in protein hydrolysates is a good example of the use that can be made of combined radiometric and isotope dilution techniques. In one procedure, the amino-acids are made to react quantitatively with excess *p*-iodobenzene sulphonyl chloride-I 131 (pipsyl chloride-I 131) in presence of sodium bicarbonate to remove excess acid. The $^{131}$I labelled pipsyl amino-acids are treated with known masses of pipsyl amino-acids labelled with sulphur-35, and the excess pipsyl chloride is removed by solvent extraction. The mixture is then separated by two-dimensional paper chromatography, and each radioactive spot is counted with and without an aluminium filter in position, to give the activities due to $^{131}I$ and ($^{131}I + ^{35}S$) respectively. In this way any loss of sulphur-35 activity during separation and extraction can be measured and corrected for (Keston *et al.*, 1950).

The technique described above could be used to determine the amino-acids present in 0·2–1 mg of protein. Later modifications can be used with samples of protein weighing as little as 1 $\mu$g. They involve (1) acetylation of the amino-acids with acetic anhydride-H3, addition of known masses of acetyl amino-acids-Cl4 and separation by paper chromatography and electrophoresis, or (2) reaction of the amino-acids with 1-fluoro-2,4-dinitrobenzene-H3, addition of known masses of amino-acid derivatives of 1-fluoro-2,4-dinitrobenzene-Cl4, and separation by paper chromatography.

For further details of applications discussed in this chapter, see reviews by Broda and Schonfield, 1966; Lambie, 1964; McMillan, 1967; Gorsuch, 1968; and Cook and Duncan, 1968.

## References

ALIMARIN, I. P., GIBALO, I. M., and SIROTINA, I. A. (1957). *Int. J. Appl. Radiat. Isotopes*, **2,** 117.

BRAUN, T., and TOLGYESSY, J. (1964). *Talanta*, **11,** 1277.

BRODA, E., and SCHÖNFELD, T. (1966). *The Technical Applications of Radioactivity*. Pergamon.

CHLECK, D., BRONSAIDES, F., SULLIVAN, W., and ZIEGLER, C. A. (1960). *Int. J. Appl. Radiat. Isotopes*, **7,** 182.

CHLECK, D., MAEHL, R., and CUCCHIARA, O. (1965). *Chemist Analyst*, **54,** 84.

CHLECK, D., MAEHL, R., CUCCHIARA, O., and CARNEVALE, E. (1963). *Int. J. Appl. Radiat. Isotopes*, **14,** 581, 593 and 599.

CRAMER, W. A., HOUTMAN, J. P. W., KOCH, R. O., and PIET, G. J. (1966). *Int. J. Appl. Radiat. Isotopes*, **17,** 97.

CURRIE, L. A., FRANCE, G. M., and STEINBERG, H. L. (1965). *Int. J. Appl. Radiat. Isotopes*, **16,** 1.

DUNCAN, J. F., and COOK, G. B. (1968). *Isotopes in Chemistry*. Oxford University Press.

DUNCAN, J. F., and THOMAS, F. G. (1957). *J. Inorg. Nucl. Chem.*, **4,** 376.

EVANS, C., and HERRINGTON, J. (1962). *Radio Isotopes in the Physical Sciences and Industry*, II, 309, I.A.E.A., Vienna.

GORSUCH, T. T. (1968). 'Radioactive Isotope Dilution Analysis'. *R.C.C. Review* 2, Radiochemical Centre, Amersham, England.

HALES, C. N., and RANDLE, P. J. (1963). *Biochem. J.*, **88,** 137.

HEVESEY, G., and HOBBIE, R. (1932). *Z. Analyt. Chem.*, **88,** 1.

HOLROYD, R. A., and KLEIN, G. W. (1962). *Int. J. Appl. Radiat. Isotopes*, **13,** 493.

KESTON, A. S., UDENFRIEND, S., and LEVY, M. (1950). *J. Am. Chem. Soc.*, **72,** 748.

LAMBIE, D. A. (1964). *Techniques for the Use of Radioisotopes in Analysis* Spon.

MAEHL, R., CUCCHIARA, O., and CHLECK, D. (1965). *Chemist Analyst*, **54,** 83.

McMILLAN, J. W. (1967). *Analyst, Lond.*, **92,** 539.

MIKHEYEVA, L. M., and MIKHEYEV, N. B. (1961). *Radioactive Isotopes in Analytical Chemistry*. Moscow.

MOYER, J. D., and ISBELL, H. S. (1958). *Analyt. Chem.*, **30,** 1975.

OVERTON, K. H. (1963). *Technique of Organic Chemistry*, **9,** 1, edited by Bentley, K. W. Interscience.

RICHTER, H. G., and GILLESPIE, A. S. (1962). *Analyt. Chem.*, **34,** 1116.

RICHTER, H. G., and GILLESPIE, A. S. (1965). *Analyt. Chem.*, **37,** 1146.

ROSENBLUM, C. (1957). *Analyt. Chem.*, **27,** 1740.

ROSS, H. H., and LYON, W. S. (1965). *Proc. Sympos. Radiochemical Methods*, **2,** 385. I.A.E.A., Vienna.

RUZICKA, J., and STARY, J. (1964). *Talanta*, **11,** 697.

RUZICKA, J., and WILLIAMS, M. (1965). *Talanta*, **12,** 967.

SCHWARZ, J. C. P. (1964). *Physical Methods in Organic Chemistry*. Oliver & Boyd.

SCOTT, B. F., and DRISCOLL, W. J. (1961). *Nucleonics*, **19,** no. 6, 49.

SEAMAN, W., and STEWART, D. (1964). *Int. J. Appl. Radiat. Isotopes*, **15,** 565.

SHEFNER, A. M., EHRLICH, R., and EHRMANTRAUT, H. C. (1967). *Int. J. Appl. Radiat. Isotopes*, **2,** 91.

SORENSEN, P. (1957). *Determination of Organic Compounds by C1-36 Isotope Dilution Analysis*. J. Gjellerups Forlag, Copenhagen.

VAN ERKELENS, P. C. (1953). *Nature, Lond.*, **172,** 357.

WALLACE, C. H., and WILLARD, J. E. (1950). *J. Am. Chem. Soc.*, **72,** 5275.

# CHAPTER 5

# Equilibrium Studies with Isotopes

The rates of chemical reactions are usually studied in reacting systems, that is, those which are not in equilibrium. The use of tracers allows us to make measurements at equilibrium from which information on rates of reaction can be deduced. Thus while the rates of reaction can often be measured by conventional techniques, they can only be studied at or near equilibrium by tracer methods.

Similar conditions apply to the study of diffusion, In classical studies of diffusion, the rate of movement of a substance is measured across a concentration gradient. This is often unsatisfactory, as when the diffusion coefficient varies with concentration. However, by using tracers, measurements of diffusion rates are possible in systems without concentration gradients, i.e. systems in equilibrium. It is even possible to make measurements of self-diffusion, as in the study of the diffusion of tritiated water into labelled water. Self-diffusion cannot be measured by classical methods.

**Self-diffusion in solids**

The first measurements of self-diffusion were made in 1921 by Groh and Hevesy. These workers welded a bar of lead labelled with $^{210}Pb$ to a bar of normal lead. Since self-diffusion is a slow process, the composite bar was heated just below its melting point in order to obtain measurements in a reasonably short time. Finally the bar was cut into sections, and the specific activity $s$ of each section plotted as a function of distance $x$ from the original weld. The diffusion coefficient $D$ can be obtained by integrating Fick's law, i.e.

$$\frac{ds}{dt} = D\frac{d^2s}{dx^2}$$

with respect to $t$.

Many variants of this technique have been proposed (Shewmon, 1963). Methods of sectioning bars have improved so that sections 5 $\mu$m thick can be obtained, for example, by electrolytic polishing or precision lathe-turning for metals. Even thinner sections, down to 1 $\mu$m thick, may be obtained by precision grinding, or by splitting ionic crystals with a microtome (Tomizuka, 1959). It is often more

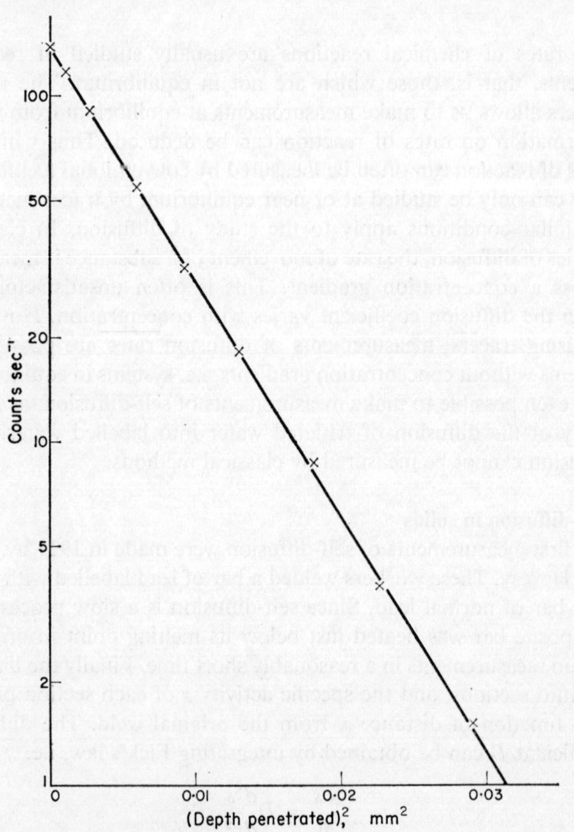


FIG. 5.1 Self-diffusion of copper measured using $^{64}$Cu at 839°C. (After A. Kuper *et al.*, (1954) *Phys. Rev.* **96**, 1 224

convenient to plate a thin layer of radioactive metal onto the end of a metal bar than it is to label the whole bar. In this case the integrated form of Fick's law takes the form

$$s_t/s_0 = 0{\cdot}5\,(\pi Dt)^{-\frac{1}{2}} \exp(-x^2/4Dt)$$

where $s_t$ is the activity of a section of bar distance $x$ from the initially active section at time $t$. Hence the diffusion coefficient $D$ can be obtained by plotting the logarithm of the specific activity against the square of the distance moved (Fig. 5.1). Diffusion coefficients in solids are quite small, even at high temperatures: published values range from $10^{-7}$ cm² s⁻¹ to $<10^{-21}$ cm² s⁻¹ (Table 5.1; Jost, 1960; Nachtrieb *et al.*, 1958). They are useful in a wide range of studies, including rates of solid reactions, heterogeneous catalysis, semi-

TABLE 5.1

Values of self-diffusion coefficients and energies of activation for pure elements, obtained by tracer experiments

| Element | $T$/°C | $D_T$/cm² s⁻¹ | $D_0$/cm² s⁻¹ | $E$/eV | Reference |
|---|---|---|---|---|---|
| Ag | 630 | $8{\cdot}6 \times 10^{-12}$ | 0·40 | 1·91 | Shewmon, 1963 |
| Au | 704 | $4{\cdot}2 \times 10^{-11}$ | 0·091 | 1·81 | Shewmon, 1963 |
| Be* | 563 | $6{\cdot}6 \times 10^{-11}$ | 0·52 | 1·63 | Dupouy +, 1966 |
| Bi* | 212 | $1{\cdot}0 \times 10^{-17}$ | 0·001 | 1·34 | Jost, 1960 |
| Cd* | 267 | $2{\cdot}0 \times 10^{-9}$ | 0·10 | 0·83 | Wajda +, 1955 |
| Co | 1050 | $3{\cdot}2 \times 10^{-12}$ | 0·37 | 2·90 | Nix and Jaumot, 1951 |
| Cu | 660 | $2{\cdot}5 \times 10^{-12}$ | 0·20 | 2·04 | Shewmon, 1963 |
| α-Fe | | | 118 | 2·91 | Shewmon, 1963 |
| Ge | | | 7·8 | 2·97 | Shewmon, 1963 |
| liq. Hg | 20 | $7{\cdot}0 \times 10^{-8}$ | | | Jost, 1960 |
| Mg* | | | 1·0 | 1·40 | Shewmon, 1963 |
| Na | 0 | $9{\cdot}2 \times 10^{-10}$ | 0·24 | 0·45 | Shewmon, 1963 |
| Nb | | | 12 | 4·55 | Shewmon, 1963 |
| Ni | 675 | $7{\cdot}5 \times 10^{-16}$ | 1·9 | 2·90 | Wazzan +, 1965 |
| Pb | 174 | $4{\cdot}8 \times 10^{-13}$ | 0·28 | 1·05 | Shewmon, 1963 |
| Se | | | 0·00014 | 0·50 | Abdullaev +, 1957 |
| Tl* | 150 | $8{\cdot}3 \times 10^{-13}$ | 0·40 | 0·98 | Shirn, 1955 |
| U* | 640 | $1{\cdot}8 \times 10^{-14}$ | | | Rothman, 1962 |
| γ-U* | 800 | $5{\cdot}0 \times 10^{-9}$ | 0·0018 | 1·19 | Shewmon, 1963 |
| Zn* | 355 | $3{\cdot}6 \times 10^{-9}$ | 0·046 | 0·88 | Jost, 1960 |
| β-Zr | | | 0·0024 | 1·65 | Shewmon, 1963 |

* = anisotropic

conductor junctions and recrystallization (e.g. in geochemistry). For example, at 910°C (the transition temperature), the rate of self-diffusion in body-centred cubic α-iron is a hundred times greater than in cubic close-packed γ-iron. Recently a small isotope effect has been found when $^{22}Na$ and $^{24}Na$ have been used to measure diffusion in sodium (Barr and Mundy, 1965).

The work of Tingley (1965) illustrates the degree of refinement of modern diffusion studies. Using single crystals of silver suspended in a solution containing silver nitrate labelled with $^{110}Ag$, this author was able to demonstrate different rates of diffusion into different faces of the crystal. The rate-determining step at room temperatures was thought to be diffusion along grain boundaries, which is a slow process with $D$ in the range 0·6–2·1 $\times 10^{-21}$ cm$^2$ s$^{-1}$.

The variation of diffusion constant with temperature can be used to find the activation energy $E$ needed to extract an atom from a lattice site, from the relation

$$D_T = D_0 \exp(-E/kT)$$

where $D_0$ is a constant and $k$ is Boltzmann's constant (8·617 $\times 10^{-5}$ eV K$^{-1}$).

Other methods of measuring diffusion coefficients of solids have been used, e.g. counting the bar itself rather than the sections removed from it, but these are subject to certain errors (Tomizuka, 1959). A different technique was used by Hevesy and Seith (1929) for alpha-emitters. Lead-212 was allowed to diffuse into lead chloride or lead iodide crystals at 400°–500°C. This isotope has a complex decay scheme

$$^{212}\text{Pb} \xrightarrow[10\cdot6\,\text{hr}]{\beta^-} {}^{212}\text{Bi} \begin{cases} \xrightarrow[1\,\text{hr}]{\alpha} {}^{208}\text{Tl} \xrightarrow[3\cdot1\,\text{min}]{\beta^-} {}^{208}\text{Pb stable} \\ \xrightarrow{\beta^-} {}^{212}\text{Po} \xrightarrow[\text{fast}]{\alpha} {}^{208}\text{Pb stable} \end{cases}$$

and the $^{208}Tl$ atoms are produced with a recoil energy of 100 keV, which is more than sufficient to volatilize them from the surface of the solid. If the parent lead atom has diffused into the bulk of the solid, the daughter $^{208}Tl$ atoms may not be able to escape. Hence the depth of penetration of the lead atoms can be calculated from measurements of the alpha-activity of the solid surface at successive times.

Diffusion in amorphous and molecular solids has also been studied, e.g. the self-diffusion of solid cyclohexane-Cl4 (Hood and Sherwood, 1965) and the diffusion of $^{24}Na$ in hot glass (Johnson *et al.*, 1951; Frischat and Oel, 1966). Self-diffusion studies in polymers have been made, and give values of $D$ in the range $10^{-11}$–$10^{-13}$ $cm^2\ s^{-1}$ at room temperature (Crank and Park, 1968).

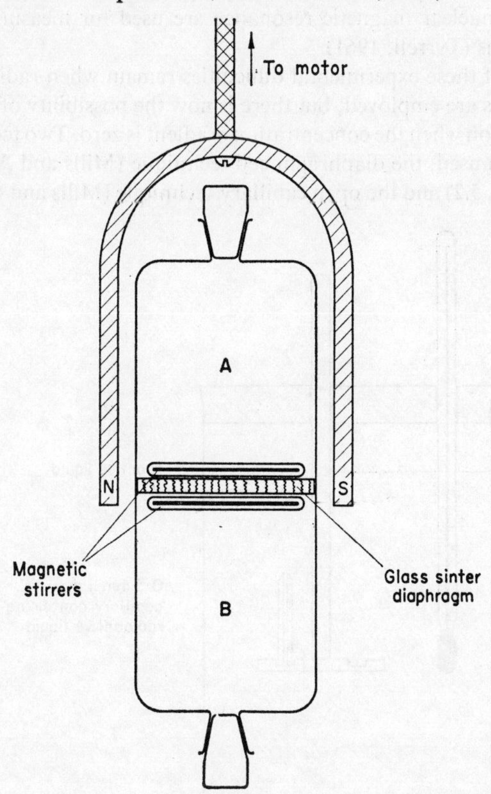


FIG. 5.2. Diaphragm cell for measuring diffusion between two liquids: volume 100 ml

**Diffusion in liquids**

In classical diffusion measurements, experimental difficulties include those of producing and maintaining a sharp boundary between two solutions of different concentrations, and of making measurements of these concentrations without disturbing the system. Very small temperature changes, or mechanical vibrations, may mix the two solutions more effectively than could unassisted diffusion. Physical measurements such as refractive index, electrical conductivity or nuclear magnetic resonance are used for measuring concentrations (Tyrrell, 1961).

Most of these experimental difficulties remain when radioisotope techniques are employed, but there is now the possibility of measuring diffusion when the concentration gradient is zero. Two techniques have been used, the diaphragm cell technique (Mills and Adamson 1955; Fig. 5.2) and the open capillary technique (Mills and Godbole

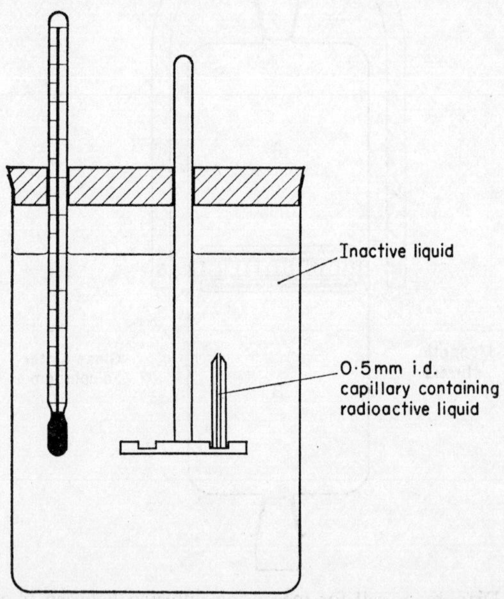


FIG. 5.3. Open capillary cell for measuring self-diffusion in liquids

1958 and 1959; Fig. 5.3). In the diaphragm cell, a labelled solution is allowed to diffuse through a sintered glass disc, with pores between 2 and 5 $\mu$m in diameter, into a large volume of inactive liquid. Alternatively an open-ended glass capillary of diameter about 0·85 mm containing about 10 $\mu$l of labelled solution, may be used. In each case the labelled solution is held in the well of a scintillator crystal so that the rate of loss of activity can be continuously recorded. Great care is taken to keep the temperature constant and to reduce extraneous vibrations. The outer solution must be stirred, but turbulent flow must be avoided and mechanical dragging of the solution out of the capillary or sintered disc is minimized by a system of baffles. The activity $a_t$ after $t$ seconds is given by

$$a_t = \frac{8}{a_0\pi^2} \sum_{n=0}^{\infty} \frac{(-1)^n}{(2n+1)^2} \exp\left[-(2n+1)^2\pi^2 Dt/4l^2\right]$$

where $D$ is the diffusion coefficient in cm$^2$ s$^{-1}$ and $l$ the length of the capillary in cm. If $Dt/l^2 > 0{\cdot}2$, only the term with $n = 0$ need be considered, i.e.

$$a_t = \frac{8}{a_0\pi^2} \exp(-\pi^2 Dt/4l^2)$$

so that the diffusion coefficient can be obtained by plotting log $a_t$ against time. $D$ usually lies between 0·8 and 3·6 $\times$ 10$^{-5}$ cm$^2$ s$^{-1}$ for dilute aqueous solutions, and is of the same order for molten salts (Borucka *et al.*, 1956), but is one or two orders of magnitude lower for viscous solutions. Radioactive techniques are among the most accurate methods of measuring the diffusion coefficients of liquids, and have been used, for example, to show that the diffusion coefficient decreases in concentrated solutions of strong electrolytes (Mills, 1961; Starik and Yuntov, 1964).

**Diffusion in gases**

Diffusion coefficients in gases at N.T.P. are of the order of 0·1–0·8 cm$^2$ s$^{-1}$, and are fairly readily measured by classical techniques (Jost, 1960). Self-diffusion can be studied using mass spectrometry and gases labelled with stable isotopes (Winn, 1950). As a result, not much work has been carried out using radioisotopes apart from studies with carbon dioxide-C14 and the inert gases argon and xenon (Hutchinson, 1947; Amdur, *et al.*, 1952; Amdur and Schatzki, 1957). In the work of Amdur *et al.*, two ionization counters containing inactive $CO_2$ and $^{14}$C-labelled $CO_2$ at the same temperature and pressure were connected together by removing a sliding valve. The ionization current $I_t$ in the labelled counter at time $t$ was given by

$$I_t = I_0[1 - A\sqrt{(Dt)}]$$

where $A$ is a parameter determined by the dimensions of the apparatus. Self-diffusion coefficients can be obtained with a precision of ±1% in this way, and can be used to test theories of intermolecular interactions in gases.

**Chemical exchange reactions**

Consider a reversible reaction of the type

$$^*AB + AC \rightleftharpoons AB + {}^*AC$$

where *A represents a radioisotopically labelled form of the atom A. If no isotopic label were present, the reaction would be trivial, and also physically undetectable. With measurable amounts of tracer present, it is possible to obtain information on the rate of exchange from studies at equilibrium.

Let rate of reaction (total number of exchanges occurring per second) = $R$ mol l$^{-1}$ s$^{-1}$

concentration of *AB = $x$ mol l$^{-1}$
concentration of *AC = $y$ mol l$^{-1}$
concentration of *A = $x + y = a$ mol l$^{-1}$
concentration of (AB + *AB) = $b$ mol l$^{-1}$
concentration of (AC + *AC) = $c$ mol l$^{-1}$

Then
$$\frac{dx}{dt} = \frac{Ry}{c}\left(\frac{b-x}{b}\right) - \frac{Rx}{b}\left(\frac{c-y}{c}\right)$$
$$= R\left(\frac{a}{c} - \frac{(b+c)x}{bc}\right)$$

In order to integrate, we need boundary conditions for $x$ and $t$. Assume that the tracer was originally added as *AC, so that $x = 0$

at $t = 0$. As $t \to \infty$, equilibrium implies that

$$x_\infty = \frac{ab}{b + c}$$

$$y_\infty = \frac{ac}{b + c}$$

Integrating between $t = 0$ and $t = \infty$, we obtain

$$1 - \frac{x}{x_\infty} = \exp -[(b + c)Rt/bc]$$

or $$\log_e(1 - x/x_\infty) = -(b + c)Rt/bc$$

Hence the rate of reaction may be obtained by plotting log $(1 - x/x_\infty)$ against time, without any assumptions about the mechanism of the reaction.

The half-time of exchange $t_{\frac{1}{2}}$ is obtainable by substituting $x = 0{\cdot}5x_\infty$ in the above equation, which yields

$$t_{\frac{1}{2}} = \frac{0{\cdot}693bc}{(b + c)R}$$

Half-times vary from microseconds to many years in practice.

If the exchange reaction is bimolecular with respect to the reacting species, which may be tested by measuring $R$ as a function of both $b$ and $c$, we can write

$$R = kbc$$

where $k$ is called the rate constant. Hence

$$k = \frac{0{\cdot}693}{(b + c)t_{\frac{1}{2}}}$$

**Techniques for equilibrium rate studies**

The isotope technique just outlined can be used for reactions with half-times between 30 seconds and a few years. Two compounds which are believed to exchange are mixed and brought to equilibrium in a thermostat. A small amount of one compound labelled with tracer of high specific activity is added, and after a known interval of time the reaction is stopped, e.g. by rapid freezing and/or separation of one or other component in good yield. Solvent extraction or volatilization are commonly used separation procedures, but in some cases the separation procedure may induce exchange. The extent of the exchange is determined by counting the component separated, with corrections for any losses in the separation procedure and also for radioactive decay. The experiment is repeated using a range of time intervals. A complete study of a reaction involves determining not merely the rate and half-time at a given temperature, but also the variation of the rate with temperature and the concentrations of reactants. Frequently, supposedly inert species may function as catalysts, and heterogeneous catalysis by glass surfaces is not rare. The main disadvantage is the need for separation before each point on the graph of specific activity (or log $(1 - x/x_\infty)$) against time can be plotted.

Stranks and Wilkins (1957) have summarized a number of difficulties which occur in this approach. These appear as either

(1) At $t = 0, x \neq 0$

or (2) $\log (1 - x/x_\infty)$ is not a linear function of $t$.

Case (1) may arise when there are two non-equivalent sets of atoms in the molecule. For example, Downs and Johnson (1955) showed that three of the five chlorine atoms in phosphorus pentachloride exchange very rapidly with chlorine-Cl36 in carbon tetrachloride; the other two atoms exchange slowly. A third component may similarly complicate the issue. Mercury(I) exchanges very rapidly with mercury(II) in solution, but in the presence of cyanide ions only the uncomplexed Hg(II) exchanges rapidly; $HgCN^+$ and $Hg(CN)_2$ exchange slowly with Hg(I) (Wolfgang and Dodson, 1952). Apparent zero time exchange may be induced by the separation procedure, e.g. when Tl(III) is separated from Tl(I) by precipitating $Tl(OH)_3$ (Prestwood and Wahl, 1949). Hence it is advisable to test more than one separation procedure for mutual consistency.

Case (2) is less common, but may arise owing to unsuspected slow reactions between one of the reactants and the solvent, or to catalysis by an impurity such as oxygen.

For reactions with half-times between 0·001 and 30 seconds, some form of flow method may be used (Roughton and Chance, 1963). An outline of the apparatus used is shown in Fig. 5.4. The reaction takes place in a mixing device such as a three-way tap $T_1$, to which labelled *AB and AC are supplied by simultaneous pressure on two syringes. The reactants pass down a length *l* of tubing before meeting a quenching solution Q in a second mixer or three-way tap $T_2$. The quenching solution stops the reaction, and the quenched mixture is removed for separation and counting. The reaction-time can

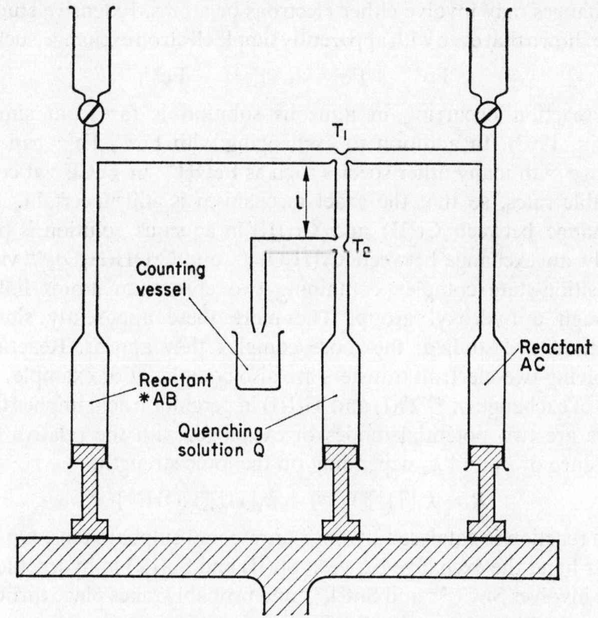


FIG. 5.4. Apparatus for the study of fast reactions

be varied by altering the length *l*. The main experimental difficulty is to find a suitable quenching solution.

An example of such a reaction is the exchange between ferrocyanide and ferricyanide ions, studied by Deck and Wahl (1954). The quenching solution used was 0·06M tetraphenyl arsonium chloride in chloroform, 0·002M in sodium hexacyanocobalt(III), and for 0·002M reagents the half-time of exchange was found to be about 0·3 second. In this case the ferrocyanide ions were separated by co-precipitation with lead hexacyanoruthenate(II), and the zero time exchange was 80%. Still faster reactions cannot as yet be measured by isotopic techniques.

The results of isotope exchange studies are now voluminous and have been reviewed several times (Amphlett, 1954; Stranks and Wilkins, 1957; Sutin, 1962; Herber, 1962; Duncan and Cook, 1968). Exchanges may involve either electrons or atoms. Extensive studies have shown that even with apparently simple electron exchange, such as

$$^{59}Fe^{2+} + Fe^{3+} \rightleftharpoons {}^{59}Fe^{3+} + Fe^{2+}$$

the reaction occurring in aqueous solution is far from simple (Sutin, 1962). In addition to exchanging with $Fe^{3+}$, $Fe^{2+}$ can exchange with many other species such as $FeOH^{2+}$ or $FeCl^{2+}$ at comparable rates, so that the exact mechanism is still uncertain. The exchange between Cr(II) and Cr(III) in aqueous solution is probably an exchange between $Cr(H_2O)_6{}^{2+}$ and $CrOH(H_2O)_5{}^{2+}$ via a transition-state complex containing two chromium atoms linked through a hydroxyl group. The more these apparently simple reactions are studied, the more complex they appear. Reactions involving two electron transfers are also complex. For example, the rate of exchange of $^{204}$Tl(I) and Tl(III) in perchloric acid implies that there are two potential modes of exchange, with the relative importance of $k_1$ and $k_2$ depending on the ionic strength.

$$R = k_1[Tl^+][Tl^{3+}] + k_2[Tl^+][TlOH^{2+}]$$

This reaction is catalysed by both nitrate and sulphate ions. On the other hand the exchange between Sn(II) and Sn(IV) in hydrochloric acid involves $SnCl_4{}^{2-}$ and $SnCl_6{}^{2-}$ and probably takes place through a transition-state complex $Sn_2Cl_{10}{}^{4-}$.

Atom exchange has also been widely studied (Stranks and Wilkins, 1957). and here again complexity of mechanism is the rule rather than the exception. For example, exchange of a chloride ion with a chloro-complex such as the aurichloride ion may take place by two mechanisms

(1) unimolecular, SN1

$$AuCl_4{}^- \xrightarrow{\text{slow}} AuCl_3 + Cl^-$$

$$AuCl_3{}^- + {}^{36}Cl^- \xrightarrow{\text{fast}} {}^{36}ClAuCl_3{}^-$$

(2) bimolecular, SN2

$$^{36}Cl^- + AuCl_4^- \xrightarrow{\text{slow}} {}^{36}ClAuCl_4^{2-} \xrightarrow{\text{fast}} {}^{36}ClAuCl_3^- + Cl^-$$

In practice the rate of exchange can be expressed as

$$R = k_1\,[AuCl_4^-] + k_2[AuCl_4^-]\,[Cl^-]$$

showing that both mechanisms operate simultaneously. The exchange of iodine ions with alkyl iodides has been thoroughly studied, as either type of reaction may predominate according to the nature of the alkyl group. A particularly interesting case is the exchange of magnesium-28 between magnesium bromide, magnesium diethyl and ethyl magnesium bromide (a Grignard reagent). Unfortunately the results here are equivocal, as traces of impurities may catalyse or inhibit the exchange, but experiments with very pure magnesium salts support the existence of the equilibria:

$$R_2Mg + {}^{28}MgBr_2 \rightleftharpoons RMgBr + R^{28}MgBr \rightleftharpoons R_2Mg^{28}MgBr_2$$

(Dessy *et al.*, 1964). Complete ethyl exchange occurs between $^{14}C_2H_5MgBr$ and $(C_2H_5)_2Mg$ within six hours (Vreugdenhil and Blomberg, 1965).

**Determination of formation constants of complexes**

Tracer methods have been used, though not as extensively as they might be, to measure the formation constants of metal complexes (Prue, 1966). Consider the case of cobalt oxalate as the metal complex under study. If an approximately $10^{-6}$M solution of cobalt chloride, labelled with $^{60}Co$, is dissolved in 0·1M perchloric acid and then shaken with a cation-exchange resin in the hydrogen form the reaction is

$$H_2R + Co^{2+} \rightleftharpoons 2H^+ + CoR$$

where R represents the resin.

The distribution ratio is defined by

$$D = [Co]_R/[Co]$$

while the partition coefficient is given by

$$P = [Co^{2+}]_R/[Co^{2+}]$$

$$= K_1 \frac{f_{Co^{2+}}\, f^2_{H^+R}\, [H^+]^2_R}{f_{Co^{2+}R}\, f^2_{H^+}\, [H^+]^2}$$

where $K_1$ is a constant and the *f*s are activity coefficients. The advantage of tracer work is that the partition coefficient and activity coefficients are insignificantly altered by the additions of tracer and complexing ligand, since these constitute less than 0·1% of the ions present. If a small amount of sodium oxalate is added to the solution, so little that the ionic strength is virtually unchanged, cobalt(II) oxalate is formed

$$Co^{2+} + Ox^{2-} \rightleftharpoons CoOx$$

therefore
$$[CoOx] = k[Co^{2+}][Ox^{2-}]$$

where $k$ is a formation constant.

Since $[Co]_{II} = [Co^{2+}]_{II}$

$$\frac{P}{D} = \frac{[Co]}{[Co^{2+}]} = \frac{[Co^{2+}] + [CoOx]}{[Co^{2+}]}$$

$$= 1 + k[Ox^{2-}]$$

Clearly $P = D$ when the oxalate concentration is zero. The distribution ratio $D$ is readily measured by counting aliquots of the resin and supernatant solution after a suitable shaking time; Schubert *et al.* (1958) used three-hour shaking periods.

The formation constant of cobalt(II) oxalate can be obtained by plotting $D^{-1}$ against oxalate concentration. The work of Schubert *et al.* should be consulted to see how other equilibria such as

$$Co^{2+} + HOx \longrightarrow CoHOx^{+}$$
$$Co^{2+} + 2HOx^{-} \longrightarrow CoH_2Ox_2$$
$$CoOx + Ox^{2-} \longrightarrow CoOx_2{}^{2-}$$

may be taken into account, and their formation constants determined. In this case oxalate labelled with $^{14}C$ was used to show that the resin did not absorb cobalt oxalate.

Very similar considerations apply to equilibria involving complexes distributed between two liquid phases. If the formation constants of complexes formed by a metal M reacting with a ligand L are defined by

$$k_n = \frac{[ML_n]}{[ML_{n-1}][L]}$$

and the distribution ratio $D$ is defined by

$$D = \frac{[M]_X}{[M]_W}$$

for two solvents W and X, it can be shown that

$$\frac{D_0}{D} = 1 + k_1[L] + k_2[L]^2 + \ldots$$

when $D_0$ is the distribution ratio in the absence of ligand.

Manning and Monk (1961) discuss the practical problems involved in determining formation constants of cobalt complexes of organic acids by the distribution method. The chief requirements are: (1) The organic phase must consist of a solvent and complexing agent with a very low solubility in water. (2) The complexing agent must have a high distribution coefficient for the metal ion. (3) The metal ion must be present at very low, constant, concentration ($\sim 10^{-6}$M). (4) The aqueous phase must be kept at constant ionic strength with an inert salt such as sodium chloride or perchlorate.

If the aqueous phase has specific activity $s_1$ counts $s^{-1}\,l^{-1}$ before shaking with the organic phase, and activity $s_2$ counts $s^{-1}\,l^{-1}$ after equilibration, the distribution ratio is given by

$$D = \frac{(s_1 - s_2)V_W}{s_2 V_X}$$

where $V_W$ is the volume of the aqueous phase, and $V_X$ that of the organic phase, after shaking. In the particular case of cobalt oxalate, the aqueous phase contained sodium chloride, sodium oxalate and a small quantity of $^{60}CoCl_2$ at pH 6·0. The organic phase consisted of 0·001M oxine in chloroform, and the phases were shaken together for 12 hours to ensure equilibration.

## References

ABDULLAEV, G. B., and BASHALIEV, A. A. (1957). *Zh. Tekhn. Fiz.*, **27**, 1911.

AMDUR, I., IRVINE, J. W., MASON, E. A., and ROSS, J. (1952). *J. Chem. Phys.*, **20**, 436.

AMDUR, I., and SCHATZKI, T. F. (1957). *J. Chem. Phys.*, **27,** 1049.
AMPHLETT, C. B. (1954). *Q. Rev. Chem. Soc.*, **8,** 219.
BARR, L. W., and MUNDY, J. N. (1965). A.E.R.E. Report R5049, H.M.S.O., London.
BORUCKA, A. Z., BOCKRIS, J. O'M., and KITCHENER, J. A. (1956). *J. Chem. Phys.*, **24,** 1282.
CRANK, J., and PARK, G. S. (1968). *Diffusion in Polymers*. Academic Press.
DECK, C. F., and WAHL, A. C. (1954). *J. Am. Chem. Soc.*, **76,** 4054.
DESSY, R. E., GREEN, S., and SALINGER, R. M. (1964). *Tetrahedron Lett.*, 1369.
DOWNS, J. J., and JOHNSON, R. E. (1955). *J. Am. Chem. Soc.*, **77,** 2098.
DUNCAN, J. F., and COOK, G. B. (1968). *Isotopes in Chemistry*. Oxford University Press.
DUPOUY, J. M., MATHIE, J., and ADDA, Y. (1966). *Mém. Scient. Revue Métall.*, **63,** 481.
FRISCHAT, G. H., and OEL, H. J. (1966). *Z. Angew. Phys.*, **20,** 195.
GROH, J., and HEVESY, G. (1921). *Annln. Phys.*, **65,** 216.
HERBER, R. H. (1962). *A. Rev. Nucl. Sci.*, **12,** 329.
HEVESY, G., and SEITH, W. (1929). *Z. Phys.*, **56,** 790.
HOOD, G. M., and SHERWOOD, J. N. (1966). *Molec. Crystal.*, **1,** 97.
HUTCHINSON, F. (1947). *Phys. Rev.*, **72,** 1256.
JOHNSON, J. R., BRISTOW, R. H., and BLAN, H. H. (1951). *J. Am. Ceram. Soc.*, **34,** 165.
JOST, W. (1960). *Diffusion of Solids, Liquids, Gases*. Academic Press.
MANNING, P. G. and MONK, C. B. (1961). *Trans. Faraday Soc.*, **57,** 1996.
MILLS, R. (1961). *Rev. Pure Appl. Chem.*, **11,** 78.
MILLS, R., and ADAMSON, A. W. (1955). *J. Am. Chem. Soc.*, **77,** 3454.
MILLS, R., and GODBOLE, E. W. (1958). *Aust. J. Chem.*, **11,** 1.
MILLS, R., and GODBOLE, E. W. (1959). *Aust. J. Chem.*, **12,** 102.
NACHTRIEB, N. H., *et al.* (1958). *Proc. Int. Conf. Peaceful Uses of Atomic Energy*, **20,** 104, New York.
NIX, F. C., and JAUMOT, F. E. (1951). *Phys. Rev.*, **82,** 72.
PRESTWOOD, R. J., and WAHL, A. C. (1949). *J. Am. Chem. Soc.*, **71,** 3137.
PRUE, J. E. (1966). *Ionic Equilibria*. Pergamon.
ROTHMAN, S. J. (1962). *Adv. Nucl. Sci. Technol.*, **1,** 111.
ROUGHTON, F. J. W., and CHANCE, B. (1963). *Technique of Organic Chemistry*, edited by Weissberger, A., **8,** 703. Second edition. Interscience.
SCHUBERT, J., LIND, E. L., WESTWALL, W. M., PFLEGER, R., and LI, N. C. (1958). *J. Am. Chem. Soc.*, **80,** 4799.
SHEWMON, P. G. (1963). *Diffusion in Solids*. McGraw-Hill.
SHIRN, G. A. (1955). *Acta Metall.*, **3,** 87.
STARIK, I. E., and YUNTOV, A. I. (1964). *Radiokhimiya*, no. 6, 466.
STRANKS, D. R., and WILKINS, R. G. (1957). *Chem. Rev.*, **57,** 743.

SUTIN, N. (1962). *A. Rev. Nucl. Sci.*, **12,** 285.

TINGLEY, I. I. (1965). *J. Electrochem. Soc.*, **112,** 60.

TOMIZUKA, C. T. (1959). *Methods in Experimental Physics*, **6A,** 364, edited by Lark-Horowitz, K., and Johnson, V. A. Academic Press.

TYRRELL, H. J. V. (1961). *Diffusion and Heat Flow in Liquids*. Butterworth.

VREUGDENHIL, A. D., and BLOMBERG, C. (1965). *Recl. Trav. Chim. Pays-Bas Belg.*, **84,** 828.

WAJDA, E. S., SHIRN, G. A., and HUNTINGDON, H. B. (1955). *Acta Metall.*, **3,** 39.

WAZZAN, A. R., and DORN, J. E. (1965). *J. Appl. Phys.*, **36,** 222.

WINN, E. B. (1950). *Phys. Rev.*, **80,** 1024.

WOLFGANG, R. L., and DODSON, R. W. (1952). *J. Phys. Chem.*, **56,** 782.

## CHAPTER 6

# Chemical Pathways

A very large amount of work has been carried out on the mechanisms of chemical reactions using radioisotopes. The techniques available are limited in number, but are extremely powerful and capable of clear-cut results. Duncan and Cook (1968) have emphasized that although isotopes allow the direct study of many reaction pathways, conventional studies of kinetics and their relation to experimental variables are usually needed to suggest hypothetical mechanisms. Isotope experiments can then be devised to distinguish between alternative hypotheses.

The isotope techniques described in this chapter are the following: (1) Testing the equivalence of atoms in molecules, (2) Kinetic studies, involving measurements of the specific activities of reactants and products as a function of time, (3) Direct studies of chemical pathways using labelled atoms, (4) Use of labelled initiator or terminator molecules in polymerization reactions. A fifth technique involving the application of isotope effects in reaction kinetics is also briefly mentioned.

**Testing the equivalence of atoms in molecules or complex ions**

This is a rather specialized application of isotopes, best illustrated by a few examples. Radioactive thiosulphate can be prepared by dissolving sulphur labelled with $^{35}S$ in sodium sulphite:

$$8Na_2SO_3 + {}^{35}S_8 \longrightarrow 8Na_2S_2O_3$$

Treatment with strong hydrochloric acid reprecipitates most of the sulphur, and liberates sulphur dioxide. Andersen (1936) showed that the sulphur was labelled, while the sulphur dioxide was inactive, which is compatible with the structure I for the thiosulphate ion.

$$[S{-}SO_3]^{2-}$$

I

On the other hand, when ammonium disulphide is synthesized using labelled sulphur

$$8(NH_4)_2S + {}^{35}S_8 \rightarrow 8(NH_4)_2S_2$$

the decomposition of the disulphide with hydrochloric acid yields sulphur and hydrogen sulphide with approximately equal specific activities (Voge, 1939). Hence the two sulphur atoms are equivalent and the disulphide ion has symmetry $D_{\infty h}$.

Similar studies have been used to show that the three hydrogens in phosphorous acid, $H_3PO_3$, are not equivalent. When the acid is dissolved in tritiated water and re-isolated, the activity per mole rises to the same value as that of the water, not to 1·5 times the water value as might be expected. Only two hydrogens exchange, because the acid has structure II, which contains a non-labile phosphorus–hydrogen bond.

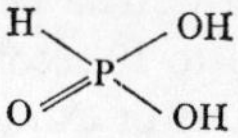

H OH
P
O OH

II

The demonstration of the equivalence of the seven carbon atoms in the tropylium ring was a particularly elegant use of isotopes. Tropylium bromide was synthesized by ring enlargement from benzene using labelled diazomethane

$$C_6H_6 \xrightarrow{*CH_2N_2} \underset{\text{cycloheptatriene}}{*C_7H_8} \xrightarrow{Br_2} \underset{\text{tropylium bromide}}{*C_7H_7Br}$$

The tropylium bromide was then reacted with phenylmagnesium bromide and finally oxidized to benzoic acid

$$*C_7H_7Br \longrightarrow *C_7H_7\phi \xrightarrow{HNO_3} \phi*CO_2H$$

The specific activity per mole of the benzoic acid was only 13·4%, or about one-seventh, of that of the diazomethane, showing that the seven ring carbons in tropylium bromide are equivalent (Volpin *et al.*, 1958 and 1959).

**Kinetic studies**

Isotopes have been used in the study of very slow reactions. For example, when alanine-1-C14 is heated it slowly loses carbon dioxide:

$$CH_3CHNH_2{}^{14}CO_2H \xrightarrow{\text{heat}} CH_3CH_2NH_2 + {}^{14}CO_2$$

The labelled carbon dioxide can be trapped and measured with much greater sensitivity of detection than can unlabelled $CO_2$. Conway and Libby (1958) have shown that the half-life of the reaction lies in the range $10^4$–0·1 years between 100° and 200°C, corresponding to a half-life of about $10^{10}$ years at room temperature. The exchange reaction between aryl iodides and potassium iodide also has a long half-life – about 400 years at room temperature according to Manno and Johnston (1957).

Very fast reactions are better studied by other techniques, but Wahl (1960) has measured the exchange between permanganate-Mn56 and manganate ions in aqueous solution, where the rate constant is 710 l $mol^{-1}$ $s^{-1}$ at 0°C. The permanganate and manganate were mixed for periods of 1 to 10 seconds, after which the reaction was quenched by precipitating or extracting the permanganate.

In a multi-stage reaction, it is possible to distinguish reactants,

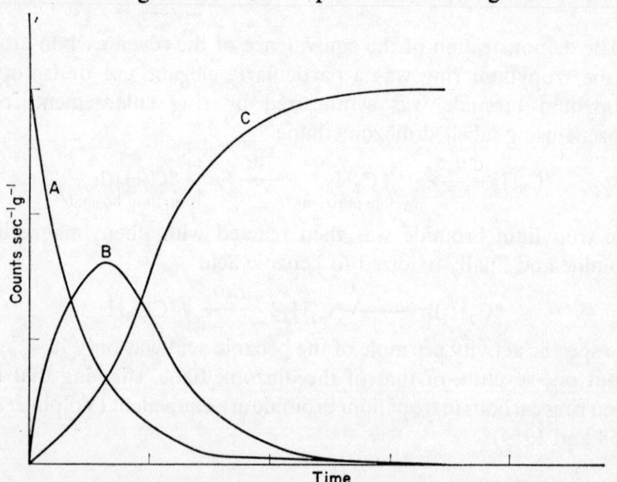


FIG. 6.1. Diagrammatic plot of specific activity against time for a chain reaction A → B → C

intermediates and products by plotting their specific activities against time. Thus if a reactant is labelled, its specific activity will fall monotonically with time, while the specific activities of labelled products will rise from zero to a final equilibrium value. On the other hand labelled intermediates will have specific activities which first rise and then fall with time, so that their curves will always have maxima (Fig. 6.1). Although these maxima may be very long and flat, it is possible to tell the three classes of compounds apart in most types of reaction (Zilversmit *et al.*, 1943; Neiman *et al.*, 1958).

A fairly straightforward example is the oxidation of methane gas at 670°C (Neiman *et al.* 1958). This reaction is fast, and it was necessary to carry out measurements by quenching at 10 millisecond intervals. The hypothesis was that the reaction occurs via the following stages:

$$CH_4 \xrightarrow{O_2} CH_2O \xrightarrow{\frac{1}{2}O_2} CO \xrightarrow{\frac{1}{2}O_2} CO_2$$

By adding formaldehyde-C14, it was possible to show that the formaldehyde concentration fell to zero within 0·15 second, while the specific activity of carbon monoxide rose and fell in the same period. These observations support the hypothesis.

A more complex example is the cyclic reaction of photosynthesis. In this reaction carbon dioxide enters the cycle, while hexose sugars leave it. The intermediate substances, none of which were proved to be intermediates prior to the studies of Calvin and Bassham (1957), do not change their concentrations, although they are all in dynamic equilibrium. Calvin and co-workers exposed cultures of the alga *Scenedesmus* to air containing carbon dioxide-C14 for short time periods, and quenched the reaction by means of boiling methanol. It was found that large numbers of compounds were labelled after exposure to $^{14}CO_2$ for 30 seconds, but that after 1 second or less only one compound was effectively labelled. This was phosphoglyceric acid (III), and subsequent degradation showed that it was exclusively labelled in the carboxyl group.

$$\begin{array}{ccc} H & & CH_2O.PO_3H_2 \\ & C & \\ HO & & {}^{14}CO_2H \end{array}$$

III

The specific activity of phosphoglycerate is at a maximum a few seconds after a one-second exposure, after which many other compounds become labelled.

By exposure to $^{14}CO_2$ for a long period, so that all intermediates were uniformly labelled, and then removing the light source, Calvin's group were able to show that the concentration of phosphoglyceric acid increased in the dark, while the concentration of another substance, ribulose 1,5-diphosphate (IV), decreased. If instead of removing the light source the labelled carbon dioxide was suddenly shut off, the specific activity of phosphoglyceric acid decreased rapidly, while the specific activity of ribulose diphosphate increased. These observations are consistent with a cyclic process of the following type:

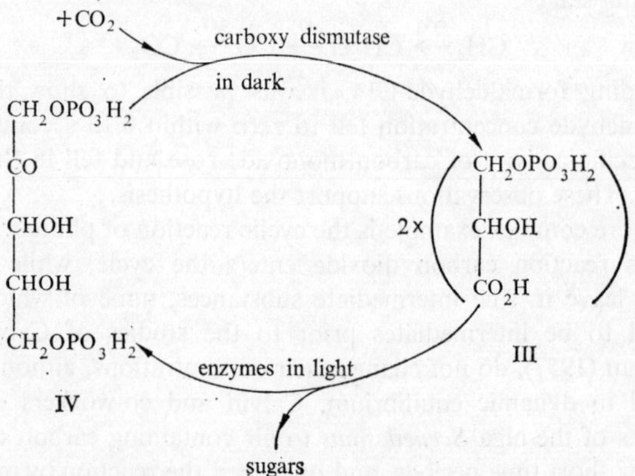


and tracer experiments have now established the details of the sequence of reactions producing IV and sugars from III and carbon dioxide in the presence of light.

**Reaction pathways: inorganic reactions**

Many inorganic reactions have been studied using tracers. For example, the presence or absence of exchange between atoms in different valency states is readily demonstrated. When potassium periodate is reacted with labelled iodides to produce iodate and iodine, it can readily be shown that only the iodine is labelled (Magnier *et al.*, 1947):

$$KIO_4 + 2\,^{128}I^- + H_2O \longrightarrow {}^{128}I_2 + KIO_3 + 2OH^-$$

In the same way, when potassium chlorate is used to oxidize labelled hydrochloric acid to chlorine, only the chlorine is labelled (Taube and Dodgen, 1949):

$$2ClO_3^- + 2\,^{36}Cl^- + 4H^+ \longrightarrow 2ClO_2 + {}^{36}Cl_2 + 2H_2O$$

Chlorine itself, when in aqueous solution, exchanges very rapidly with chloride ions, and a tracer study has shown that the reaction takes place with the trichloride ion as a transition state (Halford, 1940):

$$^{36}Cl^- + Cl_2 \rightleftharpoons {}^{36}ClCl_2^- \rightleftharpoons {}^{36}ClCl + Cl^-$$

Exchange reactions have been discussed in Chapter 5. Kinetic studies show that even apparently simple electron exchange reactions such as

$$^{59}Fe^{2+} + Fe^{3+} \rightleftharpoons {}^{59}Fe^{3+} + Fe^{2+}$$

which takes place in $\ll$ 1s in solution, is in fact a complex reaction which is not fully understood. The reaction

$$^{59}Fe(CN)_6{}^{3-} + Fe(CN)_6{}^{4-} \rightleftharpoons {}^{59}Fe(CN)_6{}^{4-} + Fe(CN)_6{}^{3-}$$

which has a half-time of the order of seconds in aqueous solution, is probably a true electron exchange.

In the study of atom or ligand exchanges, very little work has been done with aquo or ammino complexes since there are no suitable radioisotopes of nitrogen or oxygen, and tritium attached to these elements is labile. However, useful work has been done with fluoride using $^{18}F$, and with the other halogen ligands using $^{36}Cl$, $^{82}Br$ and $^{131}I$. Carbon-14 has been used to label cyanide, oxalate and carbon monoxide ligands. For example, the exchange of carbon monoxide with nickel carbonyl has been studied by Basolo and Wojcicki (1961), using toluene as a solvent.

$$^{14}CO + Ni(CO)_4 \rightleftharpoons {}^{14}CONi(CO)_3 + CO$$

Since the rate of exchange is proportional to the concentration of nickel carbonyl, but not to the concentration of carbon monoxide, the SNI dissociation of nickel carbonyl is probably the rate-determining step.

There are very few inorganic rearrangement reactions compared with the organic rearrangements discussed below. A case of some interest is the oxalato-complex of chromium(III) which is optically active but which racemizes at a measurable rate in solution. If the racemization is made to take place in a solution containing oxalic acid-C14, no radioactivity enters the complex, proving that the re-action is truly intramolecular. The corresponding complex of aluminium exchanges readily with labelled oxalate in aqueous solution.

Further details of the use of tracers in inorganic reactions will be found in reviews by Stranks and Wilkins (1957), Herber (1962), Sutin (1962), and Sykes (1966).

**Electrochemical reactions**

Surprisingly little use has been made of tracers in this field. As early as 1941, Clark and Rowan showed that lead ions are not involved in the reactions of a lead accumulator. One electrode was labelled with $^{212}Pb$ and the accumulator was put through a charge–discharge cycle: no radioactivity appeared in the electrolyte or in the other electrode. On the other hand Palagyi (1959) correlates the decline in performance of silver–zinc batteries with transport of zinc to the anode, as shown by labelling with zinc-65. Experiments on molten cryolite, using $^{26}Al$, $^{18}F$ and $^{24}Na$ have shown that most of the current is carried by the aluminium (Frank and Foster, 1957). Ogburn and Brenner (1949) have shown that electroplating of chromium from baths containing chromium(VI), does not involve chromium(III). If chromic salts containing $^{51}Cr$ are added to the bath, the label neither exchanges with the chromate nor with the deposit of metallic chromium.

An intensive study of the kinetics of the reduction of cerium(IV) perchlorate to cerium(III) perchlorate at a platinum cathode has been made using $^{141}Ce$. The reaction is complex and it appears that the actual species which is reduced is a hydroxo complex containing two cerium atoms (Fronaeus and Östman, 1956).

In recent years there has been much interest in the improvement of electroplating techniques by using minute traces of brighteners, which act by preventing the formation of large crystals. Brighteners are usually sulphur compounds, and the mechanism of 'brightening' has been studied using ammonium thiosulphate-S35 for silver (Eaton, 1955), sodium allyl sulphonate-S35 for nickel (Beacon and Riley, 1960), and N-allyl quinaldinium bromide-C14 for nickel (Doty and Riley, 1967).

**Organic rearrangements**

Carbon-14 and tritium are often used to investigate rearrangement reactions, which may occur either by an intermolecular or an intramolecular mechanism, or by both (de Mayo, 1963). Isotopic substitution has very little effect on the rates of rearrangement, and the products do not have to be isolated quantitatively. The disadvantages of the technique are that it is often difficult to synthesize an organic molecule labelled at the exact atom required, and that great care must be taken to ensure the radiochemical purity of the substance undergoing rearrangement. Some examples are given below.

When ethylamine is treated with nitrous acid to form ethanol, a small fraction of the ethyl groups rearrange, as has been shown by studies using ethylamine-1-C14 (Roberts and Yancey, 1952).

$$CH_3{}^{14}CH_2NH_2 \xrightarrow{HNO_2} \begin{cases} \xrightarrow{98{\cdot}5\%} CH_3{}^{14}CH_2OH \\ \xrightarrow{1{\cdot}5\%} {}^{14}CH_3CH^2OH \end{cases}$$

This is probably a rearrangement of the ethyl cation, i.e. a carbonium ion rearrangement.

The anilinium ion does not rearrange at room temperature, but at 150°C tritium attached to nitrogen becomes labile and substitutes the *ortho* and *para* positions (Evans, 1966).

$$C_6H_5NH_2T^+ \xrightarrow{150\,°C} o\text{-}TC_6H_4NH_3^+ + p\text{-}TC_6H_4NH_3^+$$

The Claisen rearrangement of allyl phenyl ethers has been shown to be truly intramolecular by two methods (Saunders, 1963). The reaction is

$$C_6H_5O{-}CH_2.CH{=}{}^{14}CH_2 \longrightarrow o\text{-}HOC_6H_4{-}{}^{14}CH_2.CH{=}CH_2$$

V

and the fact that the *ortho*-product is almost entirely V is good evidence that the free allyl cation or radical is not an intermediate. In addition, if two homologous labelled allyl phenyl ethers are rearranged in the same vessel, no swapping of labels takes place.

In the benzilic acid rearrangement, it has been shown that the benzyl group migrates far more readily than the phenyl group. This reaction is 100% intramolecular (Collins and Neville, 1951).

$$\phi^{14}COCOCH_2\phi \xrightarrow[(2)\ \text{heat}]{(1)\ \text{NaOH}} \phi^{14}CHOHCH_2\phi + CO_2$$

If the carbonyl next to the phenyl group is labelled, the carbon dioxide given off is inactive. If the carbonyl adjacent to the benzyl group is labelled, the carbon dioxide produced is labelled and the involatile product is inactive.

Pinacol–pinacolone rearrangements may be either intermolecular or intramolecular: they have been studied using both carbon-14 (Saunders, 1963) and tritium (Duncan and Lynn, 1957).

The reaction is:

$$R{-}C(R')(OH){-}C(R'')(OH){-}R''' \xrightarrow[-H_2O]{H^+} R{-}C(R')(R''){-}C(=O){-}R'''$$

and involves carbonium ion intermediates.

**Other organic reactions**

A great deal of tracer work has been carried out on other organic reactions. As an example, one can mention the exchange of iodide with alkyl iodides

$$^{131}I^- + RI \rightarrow {}^{131}IR + I^-$$

which has been extensively studied. This reaction may proceed by the SN2 reaction, as shown, in which case the rate is proportional to the concentrations of both RI and radioactive iodide. Alternatively, especially if R is a tertiary alkyl group, the rate-determining step may be the SN1 ionization

$$RI \rightleftharpoons R^+ + I^-$$

in which case the rate is no longer dependent on the concentration of radioactive iodide (Stranks and Wilkins, 1957).

Simple decomposition reactions are easy to study, e.g. the loss of carbon monoxide on heating esters of α-keto acids such as ethyl pyruvate. Labelling experiments prove that the carbon monoxide comes from the carboxyl group and not from the carbonyl group (Calvin and Lemmon, 1947).

$$CH_3{}^{14}COCO_2Et \xrightarrow{120°C} CH_3{}^{14}CO_2Et + CO$$

$$CH_3CO^{14}CO_2Et \xrightarrow{120°C} CH_3CO_2Et + {}^{14}CO$$

Much more complex reactions, such as the gas phase oxidation of alkanes, may be studied using techniques such as those of Neiman *et al.* (1962). These reactions involve free radicals such as methyl, ethyl, acetyl or methoxyl. Labelled radicals can be introduced into the reaction mixture by adding suitable reactants; e.g., azomethane-C14 is a source of methyl radicals:

$$^{14}CH_3N = N^{14}CH_3 \xrightarrow{heat} 2\ {}^{14}CH_3\cdot + N_2$$

acetaldehyde-C14 is a source of acetyl radicals

$$CH_3{}^{14}CHO + R\cdot \rightarrow CH_3{}^{14}CO\cdot + RH$$

By adding labelled radicals to a mixture of hydrocarbons and oxygen for a short period, quenching the reaction, separating the products by gas chromatography and determining their specific activities, much can be learnt about the reaction pathways. Neiman *et al.* (1962) showed that methyl radicals react by two competing reactions,

$$^{14}CH_3\cdot \xrightarrow{RH} {}^{14}CH_4 + R\cdot$$

$$^{14}CH_3\cdot \xrightarrow{O_2} {}^{14}CH_3OO\cdot \longrightarrow {}^{14}CH_2O,\ {}^{14}CH_3OH,\ {}^{14}CO,\ {}^{14}CO_2 \text{ etc.}$$

whose relative rates can be compared by comparing the activities of methane with the sum of the activities of oxidized products. Acetyl radicals may react either by decomposition or by oxidation:

$$CH_3{}^{14}CO\cdot \begin{cases} \longrightarrow CH_3\cdot + {}^{14}CO \\ \xrightarrow{O_2} CH_3O\cdot + {}^{14}CO_2 \end{cases}$$

and the relative rates of these processes are given by the ratio of activities of carbon monoxide and carbon dioxide in the products. Similar studies of hydrocarbon synthesis from carbon monoxide and hydrogen (Fischer–Tropsch process) are of great technical interest (Emmett, 1957).

Tritium is less often used than carbon-14 in studies of reaction mechanisms because of its lability. It has, however, been used to show that the α-hydrogen of natural amino-acids is not lost during the ninhydrin reaction (Kay and Rowland, 1959).

i.e.

$$\underset{T}{\overset{R}{}}\!>\!C\!<\!\underset{CO_2H}{\overset{NH_2}{}} + C_6H_4\!<\!\underset{CO}{\overset{CO}{}}\!>\!CO \longrightarrow \underset{T}{\overset{R}{}}\!>\!C{=}O + CO_2 + C_6H_4\!<\!\underset{CO}{\overset{C(OH)}{}}\!\!\!\geqslant\! C{-}NH_2$$

Tritium attached to oxygen or nitrogen is highly labile and even tritium attached to carbon may exchange readily. Thus tritiated acetylenic (VIa) or α-methylene groups (VIb) are labile.

$$\underset{\textbf{VIa}}{-C{\equiv}C{-}T} \qquad \underset{\textbf{VIb}}{-CO{-}CT_2{-}}$$

Fully tritiated dimethyl sulphoxide is of particular interest, in that when it is used as a solvent it will exchange tritium with very weak acids, such as the methyl group of toluene, in presence of strong bases such as potassium tert-butoxide

$$SO(CT_3)_2 + \phi CH_3 \overset{C_4H_9OK}{\rightleftharpoons} SO(CT_3)CHT_2 + \phi CH_2T$$

It has been used to measure the dissociation constant of toluene, which has a pK of about 40 (Hofmann *et al.*, 1963).

$$\phi CH_3 \rightleftharpoons \phi CH_2^- + H^+$$

**Biosynthesis**

Radioactive carbon, and to a lesser extent tritium, have been exceedingly important tools in elucidating the paths of biosynthesis and biodegradation (Wolf, 1964). The broad outlines of the mechanisms by which small molecules are synthesized are now known. Most of these, if not discovered by isotopic techniques, are readily studied by them. For example, consider the Krebs cycle involving tricarboxylic acids:

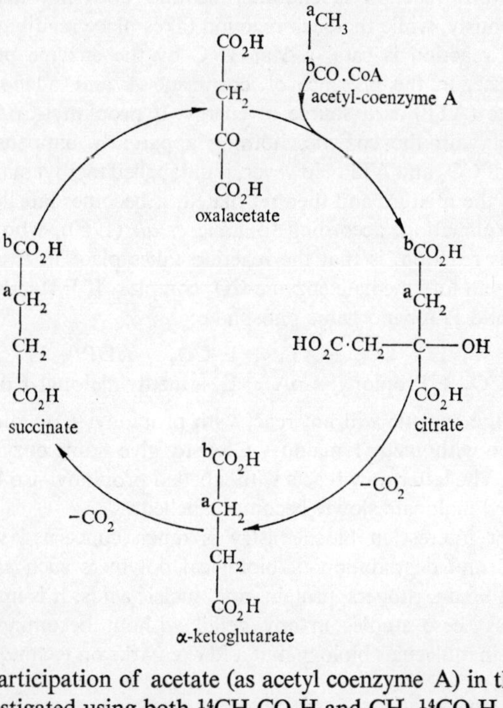

$^{a}CH_3$—$^{b}CO.CoA$ acetyl-coenzyme A

$CO_2H$—$CH_2$—$CO$—$CO_2H$ oxalacetate

$^{b}CO_2H$—$^{a}CH_2$—$C(OH)(CH_2CO_2H)$—$CO_2H$: $HO_2C{\cdot}CH_2$—C—OH citrate

$-CO_2$

$^{b}CO_2H$—$^{a}CH_2$—$CH_2$—$CO_2H$ α-ketoglutarate

$-CO_2$

$^{b}CO_2H$—$^{a}CH_2$—$CH_2$—$CO_2H$ succinate

The participation of acetate (as acetyl coenzyme A) in this cycle was investigated using both $^{14}CH_3CO_2H$ and $CH_3\,{}^{14}CO_2H$, and the fate of the atoms labelled a and b in the cycle was thereby established. Further turns of the cycle lead to further redistribution of the labelled atoms (Shemin and Wittenberg, 1951). In the same general way the biosyntheses of small molecules such as sugars, steroids, many alkaloids, amino-acids, porphyrins, purines and pyrimidines are now more or less understood. All these syntheses are mediated by highly specific enzymes, and recently isotopes have been used to investigate the mechanisms of enzymatic reactions in more detail.

As an example, consider the reaction of propionate with carbon dioxide to form methyl malonate:

$$CH_3CH_2CO_2H + CO_2 \rightleftharpoons CH_3CH(CO_2H)_2$$

The forward reaction is endothermic and does not take place spontaneously, while the back reaction takes place readily on heating. The reaction is catalysed at 37°C by the enzyme propionyl carboxylase, in the presence of coenzyme A and adenosine triphosphate (ATP) as a source of energy. If propionyl-CoA-C14 is incubated with the enzyme, nothing apparently happens in the absence of $CO_2$ and ATP. However, if unlabelled methyl malonate is added to the mixture and then reisolated, it becomes labelled.

The explanation, according to Lane *et al.* (1960), who investigated this reaction, is that the reaction takes place in two stages, involving an intermediate enzyme-$CO_2$ complex. If E stands for the enzyme and $P_i$ for inorganic phosphate:

$$E + CO_2 + ATP \rightleftharpoons E\text{–}CO_2 + ADP + P_i$$

$$E\text{–}CO_2 + \text{Propionyl–CoA} \rightleftharpoons E + \text{methylmalonyl–CoA}$$

That is, the enzyme will not react with propionyl–CoA alone, but will react with methyl malonyl–CoA to give some enzyme–$CO_2$ complex. The latter now reacts with labelled propionyl–CoA so that the methyl malonate slowly becomes labelled.

Current interest in biochemistry is much concerned with the syntheses and degradation of biological polymers such as carbohydrates, lignin, rubbers, proteins and nucleic acids. It is impossible to discuss these studies in any detail without becoming deeply involved in molecular biology, but a few remarks on techniques may be useful.

In carbohydrate synthesis, the monomeric sugars are readily labelled with carbon-14, and the sugar phosphates may be labelled with phosphorus-32. Coniferyl alcohol glucoside (VII: G = glucose) appears to be the main precursor of lignin (Freudenberg, 1965), while mevalonic acid (VIII) is an important precursor of rubber in *Hevea* sap (Gascoigne and Jones, 1959).

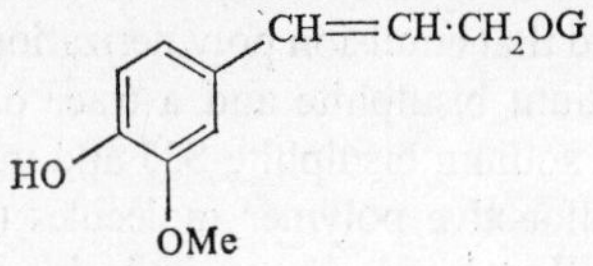

$CH{=}CH{\cdot}CH_2OG$ HO OMe

VII

HO $CH_2CO_2H$ C $CH_3$ $CH_2CH_2OH$

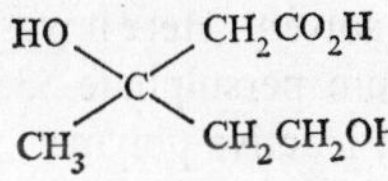

VIII

In studying protein synthesis, all the natural amino-acids are available with carbon-14 or tritium labels, while cysteine, cystine and methionine can be labelled with sulphur-35. Incorporation of $^{35}S$-labelled amino-acids into protein is a standard test for protein turnover, even in the absence of net biosynthesis. Proteins can be labelled with these two nuclides, and also by iodination with iodine-I 131, but there is no satisfactory method of labelling proteins with tritium.

The pyrimidines cytidine and thymidine are available labelled both specifically and unspecifically with tritium and/or carbon-14, and the same holds true for purines adenosine and guanosine: the phosphates of all these compounds except cytidine are available labelled with phosphorus-32. All these compounds are invaluable in studying the biosynthesis of nucleic acids.

**Polymerization**

The use of isotopes in polymerization studies has been the subject of extensive reviews (Ayrey, 1963; Bevington, 1961). Much of the work has been concerned with the mechanism of initiation and termination of the polymerization reaction. The initiation of polymerization is often carried out by adding sources of either free radicals or reactive ions to the monomer, and these sources can usually be labelled. For example, potassium persulphate is an initiator for the polymerization of emulsions of styrene in water. If the persulphate is labelled with sulphur-35, the label is incorporated into the polymer (Smith and Campbell, 1947; Kolthoff *et al.*; 1955). If it is assumed that the polymer chain is unbranched, and is both initiated and terminated by an $—SO_3H$ group, the average molecular weight of polymer can be determined from its specific activity. Such measurements are especially useful for polytetrafluoroethylene, which is soluble in no known solvent. Here it was found that emulsion polymerization with potassium persulphate-S35, sodium bisulphite and a trace of iron gave an inactive polymer, while sodium bisulphite-S35 and inactive potassium persulphate gave radioactive polymer molecules (Berry and Peterson, 1951). On the other hand when vinyl chloride is polymerized in presence of perchloric acid-Cl36 and sodium bisulphite-S35, the resulting polymer contains both labels, with about four times as much sulphur-35 as chlorine-36 (Firschung and Rosen, 1959).

The homogeneous polymerization of styrene and methyl mechacrylate have been intensively studied. The most widely used initiators are azoisobutyronitrile (IX) and diaroyl peroxides such as dibenzoyl peroxide (X)

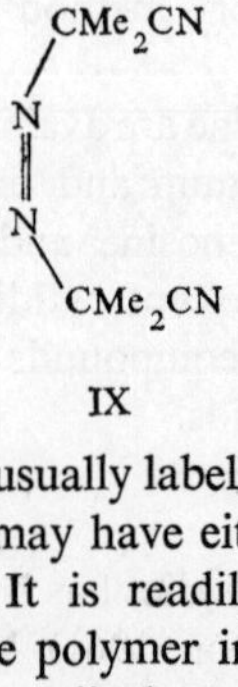

$$\begin{array}{cc} \text{CMe}_2\text{CN} & \text{CO}\cdot\text{C}_6\text{H}_5 \\ | & | \\ \text{N} & \text{O} \\ \| & | \\ \text{N} & \text{O} \\ | & | \\ \text{CMe}_2\text{CN} & \text{CO}\cdot\text{C}_6\text{H}_5 \\ \text{IX} & \text{X} \end{array}$$

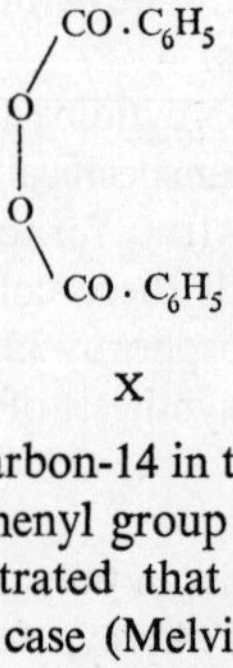

The former is usually labelled with carbon-14 in the nitrile group, while the latter may have either the phenyl group or the carboxyl group labelled. It is readily demonstrated that isobutyronitrile radicals enter the polymer in the first case (Melville, 1957), while both benzoyloxy radicals and phenyl radicals are involved in the second (Koton *et al.*, 1954; Ayrey, 1963). Once again, molecular weight determinations are possible by making hypotheses about the reaction mechanisms, which can be tested experimentally. Terminal phenyl groups are only removed with difficulty, but terminal benzoyloxy groups can be hydrolysed off under mild conditions.

Ionic polymerizations of alkenes have been studied by Natta and co-workers (1958). Triethylaluminium-C14 was absorbed onto α-titanium trichloride and used as a Ziegler catalyst to polymerize propene. The terminal groups of the polypropene were found to contain nearly all the carbon-14 label used. Solvent effects are important. When isobutene was polymerized using aluminium chloride dissolved in methyl chloride-C14 as a catalyst, about 25% of the polymer molecules were labelled, presumably via the ionization

$$^{14}CH_3Cl + AlCl_3 \rightleftharpoons {}^{14}CH_3^+ + AlCl_4^-$$

(Kennedy, 1959).

Relatively little has been done with radioisotopes in studying the propagation reaction of polymerization, except to show that the polymerization of methyl methacrylate is reversible. When purified labelled polymer was equilibrated with inactive monomer the latter slowly became radioactive (Levin *et al.*, 1959).

Kinetic studies using isotopes have given much information on the termination reaction. If this occurs by combination of two large free radicals, as in the polymerization of styrene below 60°C, the rate of termination will be proportional to the square root of the concentration of initiator. If the reaction terminates by disproportionation of large radicals, as in the polymerization of methyl methacrylate at high temperatures, the rate of termination will be proportional to the concentration of the initiator. Labelled substances have often been employed as terminators: for example either carbon dioxide-C14 or tritium acetate will terminate polymerizations involving anions thus:

$$R^- + {}^{14}CO_2 \rightarrow R^{14}CO_2^-$$
$$R^- + {}^{3}HOAc \rightarrow R^3H + OAc^-$$

Labelled retarder or inhibitor molecules such as picric acid-C14, diphenyl picryl hydrazyl-C14 and *p*-benzoquinone-C14 terminate the polymerization of styrene. The latter gives a polymer containing one quinone unit per molecule, whose structure can be shown to be XI by breaking the ether links with trifluoroacetic anhydride, which

R—O—⬡—O—R

XI

renders the polymer inactive, thus (Melville, 1957):

$$RO-C_6H_4-OR + (CF_3CO)_2O \rightarrow ROR + CF_3COO-C_6H_4-OOC.CF_3$$

Many studies have also been made of co-polymerization, graft polymerization and branching. The extent of branching can be measured as follows. Some linear polymer is made and purified. This is dissolved in labelled monomer, and polymerization is re-initiated. After a given time, the reaction is stopped, and the polymer is separated into linear and branched fractions. The average weight of branches can be calculated from the specific activity of the branched polymer fraction.

**Isotope effects**

The isotope effect is the term used to cover the small differences in behaviour between two isotopes of an element owing to their difference in mass. The effect is observed both in equilibrium and rate processes,and is largest for the isotopes of hydrogen, but is measurable for the isotopes of carbon and some heavier elements (Melander, 1960; Yakushin, 1962). Thus in the hydrolysis of phenyl magnesium bromide with tritiated water, there is a large isotope effect. If the rate constants

$$C_6H_5MgBr + HTO \begin{cases} \xrightarrow{k_H} C_6H_6 \\ \xrightarrow{k_T} C_6H_5T \end{cases}$$

are $k_H$ and $k_T$, the ratio $k_H/k_T = 1{\cdot}64$ (Assarsson, 1955). Much smaller isotope effects are observed for reactions involving carbon-12 and carbon-14, e.g.

$$H\,{}^*CO_2H \xrightarrow{H_2SO_4} {}^*CO + H_2O \quad k_{12}/k_{14} = 1{\cdot}11$$

(Ropp *et al.*, 1951)

$${}^*CH_2(CO_2H)_2 \xrightarrow{154°C} {}^*CH_3CO_2H + CO_2 \quad k_{12}/k_{14} = 1{\cdot}07$$

(Ropp and Raaen, 1952)

$$Me_2\,{}^*CHOH \xrightarrow{H_2CrO_4} Me_2\,{}^*C = O \quad k_{12}/k_{14} = 1{\cdot}035$$

(Ropp and Hodnett, 1956)

Because of the isotope effect, it is possible to separate molecules such as $CT_4$, $CHT_3$, $CH_2T_2$ and $CH_3T$ by gas chromatography on charcoal (Gant and Yang, 1964). Molecules labelled with carbon-14 have not been completely separated, but inactive glycine, glycine-1-C14 and glycine-2-C14 have been fractionated on ion-exchange columns. The slow-running fraction of the labelled glycine peak may have ten times the specific activity of the fast-running fraction (Piez and Eagle, 1956).

Isotope effects on reaction rates may often be calculated, and the results used to distinguish hypothetical reaction mechanisms. The determination of isotope effects has been reviewed by Collins (1964) and by Yakushin (1962).

## References


ANDERSEN, E. (1936). *Z. Phys. Chem.*, **32B,** 237.

ASSARSSON, L. O. (1955). *Acta Chem. Scand.*, **9,** 1399.

AYREY, G. (1963). *Chem. Rev.*, **63,** 645.

BASOLO, F., and WOJCICKI, A. (1961). *J. Am. Chem. Soc.*, **83,** 520.

BEACON, S. E., and RILEY, B. J. (1960). *J. Electrochem. Soc.*, **107,** 785.

BERRY, K. L., and PETERSON, J. H. (1951). *J. Am. Chem. Soc.*, **73,** 5195.

BEVINGTON, J. C. (1961). *Radical Polymerization*. Academic Press.

CALVIN, M., and BASSHAM, J. A. (1957). *The Path of Carbon in Photosynthesis*. Prentice Hall.

CALVIN, M., and LEMMON, R. E. (1947). *J. Am. Chem. Soc.*, **69,** 1232.

CLARK, G. L., and ROWAN, R. (1941). *J. Am. Chem. Soc.*, **63,** 1299.

COLLINS, C. J. (1964). *Adv. Phys. Org. Chem.*, **2,** 63.

COLLINS, C. J., and NEVILLE, O. K. (1951). *J. Am. Chem. Soc.*, **73,** 2471.

CONWAY, D., and LIBBY, W. F. (1958) *J. Am. Chem. Soc.*, **80,** 1077.

DOTY, W. R., and RILEY, B. J. (1967). *J. Electrochem. Soc.*, **114,** 50.

DUNCAN, J. F., and COOK, G. B. (1968). *Isotopes in Chemistry*. Oxford University Press.

DUNCAN, J. F., and LYNN, K. R. (1957). *Aust. J. Chem.*, **10,** 1.

EATON, S. A. (1956). *Proc. Int. Conf. on Peaceful Uses of Atomic Energy*, **14,** 61, New York.

EMMETT, P. H. (1957). *Adv. Catalysis*, **9,** 645.

EVANS, E. A. (1966). *Tritium and its Compounds*. Butterworths.

FIRSCHUNG, F. H., and ROSEN, I. (1959). *J. Polym. Sci.*, **36,** 305.

FRANK, W. B., and FOSTER, L. M. (1957). *J. Phys. Chem.*, **61,** 1531.

FREUDENBERG, K. (1965). *Science, N.Y.*, **148,** 595.

FRONAEUS, S., and ÖSTMAN, C. O. (1956). *Acta Chem. Scand.*, **10**, 769.
GANT, P. L., and YANG, K. (1964). *J. Am. Chem. Soc.*, **86**, 5063.
GASCOIGNE, J. A., and JONES, P. (1959). *Nature, Lond.*, **183**, 819.
HALFORD, R. S. (1940). *J. Am. Chem. Soc.*, **62**, 3233.
HERBER, R. H. (1962). *A. Rev. Nucl. Sci.*, **12**, 329.
HOFMANN, J. E., MULLER, R. J., and SCHRIESHEIM, A. (1963). *J. Am. Chem. Soc.*, **85**, 3000 and 3002.
KAY, J. G., and ROWLAND, F. S. (1959). *J. Org. Chem.*, **24**, 1800.
KENNEDY, J. P. (1959). *J. Polym. Sci.*, **38**, 263.
KOLTHOFF, I. M., O'CONNOR, P. R., and HANSEN, J. L. (1955). *J. Polym. Sci.*, **15**, 459.
KONDRATYEV, V. N. (1956). *Proc. Int. Conf. on Peaceful Uses of Atomic Energy*, **15**, 3, New York.
KOTON, M. M., KISELEVA, T. M., and BESSENOV, M. I. (1954). *Zh. Fiz. Khim.*, **28**, 2137.
LANE, M. D., HALENZ, D. R., KOSOW, D. B., and HEGRE, C. S. (1960). *J. Biol. Chem.*, **235**, 3082.
LEVIN, P. I., MILLER, V. B., NEVSKII, L. V., NEIMAN, M. B., KARGIN V. A., and RYLOV, E. E. (1959). *Trudy Khim. Khim. Tekhnol.*, **2**, 3.
MAGNIER, P., KHRAMOFF, A., MARTIN, M., and DAUDEL, P. (1947). *Bull. Soc. Chim. Fr.*, **14**, 626.
MANNO, P. J., and JOHNSTON, W. H. (1957). *J. Am. Chem. Soc.*, **79**, 807.
MAYO, P. DE (1963). *Molecular Rearrangements*. Interscience.
MELANDER, L. (1960). *Isotope Effects on Reaction Rates*. Ronald Press, New York.
MELVILLE, H. W. (1957). *Chemy. Ind.*, 1632.
NATTA, G., PAJARO, G., PASQUON, I., and STELLACCI, V. (1958). *Atti Accad. Naz. Lincei Memorie*, **24**, 479.
NEIMAN, M. B., EFREMOV, V. Y., and SERDYUK, N. K. (1962). *Int. J. Appl. Radiat. Isotopes*, **13**, 295.
OGBURN, F., and BRENNER, J. (1949). *Trans. Electrochem. Soc.*, **96**, 47.
PALAGYI, T. Z. (1959). *J. Electrochem. Soc.*, **106**, 846.
PIEZ, K. A., and EAGLE, H. (1956). *J. Am. Chem. Soc.*, **78**, 5284.
ROBERTS, J. D., and YANCEY, J. A. (1952). *J. Am. Chem. Soc.*, **74**, 5943.
ROPP, G. A., and HODNETT, E. M. (1956). *J. Chem. Phys.*, **25**, 587.
ROPP, G. A., and RAAEN, V. F. (1952). *J. Am. Chem. Soc.*, **74**, 4992.
ROPP, G. A., WEINBERGER, A. J., and NEVILLE, O. K. (1951). *J. Am. Chem. Soc.*, **73**, 5593.
SHEMIN, S., and WITTENBERG, J. (1951). *J. Biol. Chem.*, **192**, 315.
SMITH, W. V., and CAMPBELL, H. N. (1947). *J. Chem. Phys.*, **15**, 338.
STRANKS, D. R., and WILKINS, R. G. (1957). *Chem. Rev.*, **57**, 743.
SUTIN, N. (1962). *A. Rev. Nucl. Sci.*, **12**, 285.
SUTYAGINA, A. A. (1958). *Zav. Lab.*, **24**, 43.
SYKES, A. G. (1966). *Kinetics of Inorganic Reactions*. Pergamon.
TAUBE, H., and DODGEN, H. (1949). *J. Am. Chem. Soc.*, **71**, 3330.

VOGE, H. (1939). *J. Am. Chem. Soc.*, **61,** 1032.

VOLPIN, M. E., KURSANOV, D. N., SHEMYAKIN, M. M., MAIMIND, V. J., and NEIMAN, L. A. (1958). *Chemy. Ind.*, 1261.

idem (1959). *Zh. Obshch. Khim.*, **29,** 3711.

WAHL, A. C. (1960). *Z. Elektrochem.*, 64, 90.

WILKINS, R. G. (1962). *Q. Rev. Chem. Soc.*, **16,** 316.

WOLF, G. (1964). *Isotopes in Biology*. Academic Press.

YAKUSHIN, F. S. (1962). *Russ. Chem. Revs.*, **31,** 123.

ZILVERSMIT, D. B., ENTEMMANN C., and FISHER, M. C. (1943). *J. Gen. Physiol.*, **26,** 325 and 333.

# CHAPTER 7

# Miscellaneous Studies with Radioisotopes

## Autoradiography

Autoradiography is a technique in which a radioactive sample is pressed against a photographic emulsion of silver bromide crystals in gelatin. The radiation gives rise to a latent image in the emulsion, which can be developed and fixed in the usual way, so that the radiation tracks are made visible by small particles of metallic silver. Thus the process is based on the high efficiency of the solid-state reaction:

$$2AgBr \xrightarrow{h\nu} 2Ag + Br_2$$

Autoradiography has been used as a qualitative technique to find the spots on radioactive chromatograms, especially for tritium and carbon-14. For example, it has been used to locate the amino-acids derived from the hydrolysis of animal protein labelled with $^{14}C$ after separation by two-dimensional chromatography. The exposure time may be varied to obtain reasonable blackening on the emulsion. For example, a 1 $cm^2$ spot containing 1 $\mu$Ci of $^{14}C$ would need an exposure of about half an hour to give a good autoradiograph using X-ray film (Faires and Parks, 1964).

Chamberlain *et al.* (1964) have shown that 1 $\mu$Ci of $^3H$ on a paper chromatogram usually needs an exposure time of about five hours to produce a satisfactory autoradiograph. This can be reduced to less than one hour by impregnating the chromatogram with photographic emulsion, but this may lead to chemical fogging. The technique is at best semiquantitative, and has been largely superseded by chromatogram scanners using Geiger or scintillation counters as detectors. At present the main applications of the technique are in high-resolution work in metallurgy and biochemistry.

The resolution of autoradiography is the distance from a point source at which the grain density falls to half its value directly over the source. It depends on a number of factors, including the energy and range of the radiation, the thickness of the sample, the thickness of the emulsion, the distance between the sample and the emulsion, the percentage of silver bromide in the emulsion and the average grain size. The properties of some emulsions are shown in the following table (Table 7.1).

TABLE 7.1

Properties of some photographic emulsions

| Emulsion | % AgBr | Density/g $cm^{-3}$ | Thickness/$\mu$m | Grain size/$\mu$m |
|---|---|---|---|---|
| Photographic | 10–20 | 1·4–1·6 | 10–20 | 1–4 |
| Stripping film | 45 | 2·1 | (1–)5 | 0·2 |
| Nuclear | 80 | 3·6 | 0·1–1000 | 0·04–0·4 |

For high-resolution work it is desirable to use low-energy radiation, samples 0·5 $\mu$m thick or less, and fine-grain emulsions which are as thin as possible and intimately in contact with the sample. Gamma-rays are too penetrating to yield anything but coarse, macro-auto-

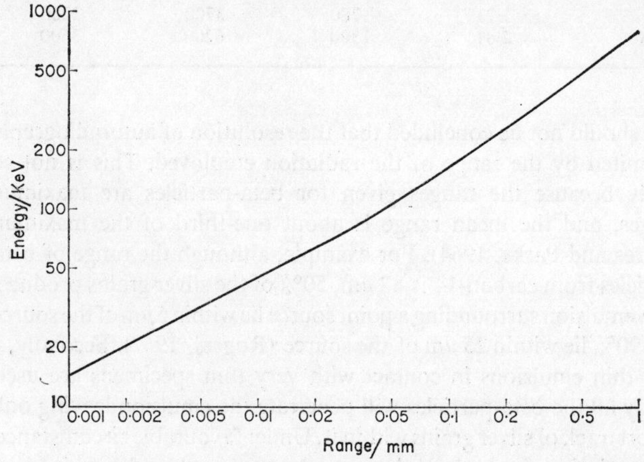


FIG. 7.1. Relationship between energy and range in nuclear emulsions for beta-particles

radiographs. Alpha-particles have a calculable range which is a function of their energy and the atomic numbers of the atoms in the emulsion. Their range is usually between 20 and 50 μm: for example the range of the 5·30 MeV alpha-particles from $^{210}$Po in high-density emulsions is 21·4 μm. The range of beta-particles is related to their energy by a complex relation shown graphically in Fig. 7.1 (Herz, 1951). Table 7.2 shows the ranges of beta-particles from various radionuclides in photographic emulsions.

TABLE 7.2
Energies and ranges of beta-particles in photographic emulsions

| Isotope | β-energy/ MeV | Mass per unit area to stop β/ mg cm$^{-2}$ | Range in stripping film/ μm | Range in nuclear emulsion/ μm |
|---|---|---|---|---|
| $^{3}$H | 0·018 | 0·57 | 2·7 | 1·6 |
| $^{63}$Ni | 0·062 | 6·2 | 30 | 17 |
| $^{14}$C | 0·155 | 29·5 | 140 | 82 |
| $^{35}$S | 0·167 | 34 | 160 | 94 |
| $^{121}$Sn | 0·38 | 115 | 550 | 320 |
| $^{99}$Mo | 1·23 | 550 | 2600 | 1500 |
| $^{32}$P | 1·71 | 780 | 3700 | 2200 |
| $^{56}$Mn | 2·81 | 1300 | 6200 | 3600 |

It should not be concluded that the resolution of autoradiography is limited by the range of the radiation employed. This is not so, firstly because the ranges given for beta-particles are maximum ranges, and the mean range is about one-third of the maximum (Faires and Parks, 1964). For example, although the range of beta-particles from carbon-14 is 82 μm, 50% of the silver grains produced in an emulsion surrounding a point source lie within 5 μm of the source, and 90% lie within 25 μm of the source (Rogers, 1967). Secondly, if very thin emulsions in contact with very thin specimens are used, nearly all the beta-particles will penetrate the emulsion leaving only a short track of silver grains within it. Under favourable circumstances the resolution can be kept down to the same order of magnitude as the combined thickness of sample and emulsion. Using an optical microscope for magnification, resolutions of 0·5–1 μm for tritium, 2–5 μm for carbon-14 or sulphur-35, and 5–10 μm for phosphorus-32 have been attained (Rogers, 1967). Still better resolution, perhaps as good as 0·07 μm, may be obtained using the electron microscope. Here exceedingly thin specimens and emulsions are required, so that the exposure time needs to be quite long (Ullberg, 1965).

**Autoradiographic techniques**

Techniques have been described by Boyd (1955), Taylor (1960) and Rogers (1967). They usually involve either a stripping-film technique or coating the sample in molten emulsion. In the former case, a thin section of sample is attached to a microscope slide. The emulsion (Kodak AR10) is stripped from its backing by floating on water at 24°C in a dark room, and the film of emulsion is then picked up on the slide. The slide is dried in a jet of cold air and stored in a light-tight box at 4°C for a suitable period before development. Alternatively, an emulsion such as Ilford L4 may be kept in a molten state at 43°C in a dark room. Samples are coated with emulsion by dipping, but it is difficult to obtain uniformly thin layers in this way. Sources of error include the development of images due to stray light sources or sources of radiation, chemical fogging which is often found with biological samples, or fogging by pressure, e.g. fingerprints. Mechanical displacements of the sample during cutting, or the leaking of radioactivity during sample preparation and handling, must also be anticipated.

**Efficiency and sensitivity of autoradiography**

If a radioactive point source was surrounded by thick layers of nuclear emulsion, virtually every beta-particle leaving the sample would leave a measurable track, so the detection efficiency would be 100%. In practice, however, the sample has a finite thickness resulting in some self-absorption, while the emulsion also has finite thickness and is difficult to examine microscopically in more than two dimensions. The effect of self-absorption is most marked with tritium, where it has been studied in samples of polymethyl methacrylate-H3; some results are given in Table 7.3 (Falk and King, 1963). In high-resolution autoradiography silver grains are

TABLE 7.3

Effect of sample thickness on autoradiography of polymethyl methacrylate-H3

| Thickness/$\mu$m | Efficiency/% |
|---|---|
| 0·5 | 15·7 |
| 1·0 | 11·1 |
| 2·0 | 7·0 |
| 5·0 | 4·2 |
| 10·0 | 2·0 |

easier to count than are radiation tracks. According to Rogers (1967), for a 5 $\mu$m sample in contact with a 2 $\mu$m emulsion, the number of silver grains found in the emulsion per disintegration in the sample is about 0·3 for carbon-14, sulphur-35 and phosphorus-32, but only 0·02 for tritium. Current work with nuclear emulsions involves the detection of as little as 1 disintegration per day, so the potential sensitivity of autoradiography is very high.

**Applications of autoradiography**

Metallurgical applications have been reviewed by Ward (1960). They include studies of mass-transfer, diffusion, rates of crystallization and electrodeposition, and alloy formation, most of which can and have also been investigated by counting techniques. Biochemical applications have been reviewed by Boyd (1955) and Rogers (1967). They include the localization of polymeric molecules in cells by labelling with suitable active monomers. A truly chemical application has been described by Moyer and Ochs (1963). These authors synthesized polyethylene and polystyrene labelled with tritium, and used autoradiography as a means of demonstrating regularities in the structures of these apparently amorphous polymers.

**Solid-state transitions and reactions**

Two isotopic techniques have been used to study transitions in solids. The first, or *emanation technique*, was first applied by Hahn and Müller (1923). If a solid is labelled with a radioactive gas, the rate at which the gas escapes by diffusion depends on temperature, and the plot of rate against temperature changes its slope at temperatures where solid transitions or reactions occur. A sample of labelled solid is heated in a stream of argon, and the count-rate or 'emanating power' of the gas stream is measured. Thus Jech (1960) studied the dehydration of calcium sulphate dihydrate using $^{85}$Kr

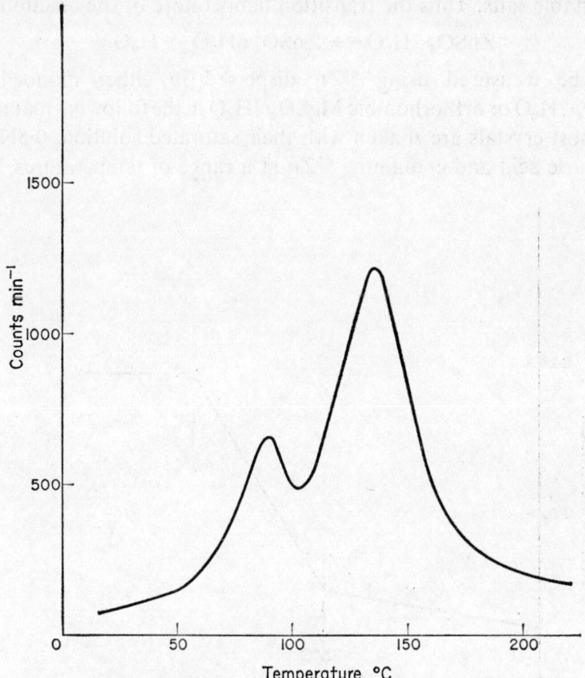


FIG. 7.2. Release of radon-222 from calcium sulphate dihydrate on heating. (After Jech, 1960)

and $^{222}$Rn (Fig. 7.2). Other workers have labelled the solid with nuclides which decay to give radioactive gases, e.g.

$$^{228}\text{Th} \underset{t_{\frac{1}{2}}=1{\cdot}9\ \text{yr}}{\longrightarrow} {}^{224}\text{Ra} \underset{t_{\frac{1}{2}}=3{\cdot}6\ \text{d}}{\longrightarrow} {}^{220}\text{Rn}\ (t_{\frac{1}{2}}=54\ \text{s}) \quad \text{(Shabowra and Shibanowa, 1965)}$$

$$^{226}\text{Ra}\ (t_{\frac{1}{2}}=1620\ \text{yr}) \longrightarrow {}^{222}\text{Rn}\ (t_{\frac{1}{2}}=3{\cdot}8\ \text{d}) \quad \text{(Kaiser, 1954)}$$

$$^{132}\text{Te}\ (t_{\frac{1}{2}}=78\ \text{hr}) \longrightarrow {}^{132}\text{I}\ (t_{\frac{1}{2}}=3{\cdot}2\ \text{hr}) \quad \text{(Cook and Prout, 1956)}$$

However, this technique gives little information that cannot be gleaned from thermogravimetric analysis, and is seldom used.

Purkayastha and Sarkar (1966) have proposed an ingenious method for measuring transition temperatures in unstable or metastable salts. Thus the transition temperature of the reaction

$$ZnSO_4{\cdot}7H_2O \longrightarrow ZnSO_4{\cdot}6H_2O + H_2O$$

may be measured using $^{65}Zn$ dispersed in either monoclinic $FeSO_4{\cdot}7H_2O$ or orthorhombic $MgSO_4{\cdot}7H_2O$ in the following manner. The host crystals are shaken with their saturated solution, 0·5N in sulphuric acid and containing $^{65}Zn$ at a range of temperatures, for

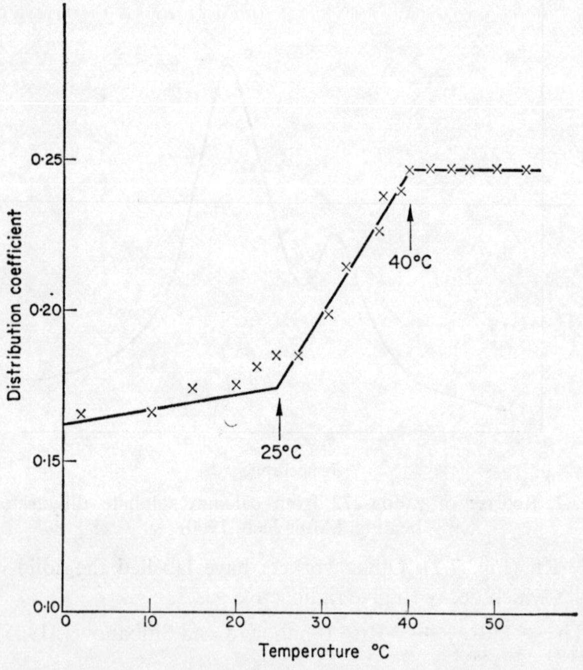


FIG. 7.3. The transition temperatures of monoclinic zinc sulphate hydrate determined using tracer $^{65}Zn$ in iron(II) sulphate heptahydrate. (After Purkayastha and Sarkar, 1966)

sufficient time to ensure equilibrium (about 96 hours). If a distribution coefficient is defined by

$$D = \frac{[^{65}Zn]_{solid} \times [FeSO_4]_{solution}}{[^{65}Zn]_{solution} \times [FeSO_4]_{solid}}$$

The plot of $D$ against $T$ changes slope at each transition temperature (Fig. 7.3). Neither ferrous nor magnesium sulphates have a transition in the range 20–50°C, but tracer studies show that monoclinic zinc sulphate has a transition at 25°C, while orthorhombic zinc sulphate has a transition at 40°C.

**Adsorption and surface area**

Radioisotopes provide a useful method of measuring the number of molecules adsorbed at a surface. If a solid is assumed to take up a monolayer of molecules, we can estimate its specific surface $S$ from

$$S = 6{\cdot}023 \times 10^8 x_m \quad A/M \text{ m}^2 \text{ kg}^{-1}$$

where $x_m$ = mass of adsorbate in g per kg adsorbent for monolayer formation.

$A$ = apparent area of adsorbate molecules in nm²

$M$ = molecular weight of adsorbate in u

In this expression $x_m$ is readily determined from measurements of radioactivity, but $A$ must be obtained by different techniques. $A$ can be put equal to $(M/\rho N)^{2/3} \times 10^{14}$ in many cases, where $\rho$ is the density of solid adsorbate in g cm$^{-3}$ and $N$ is Avogadro's constant $6{\cdot}023 \times 10^{23}$ ug$^{-1}$ (Gregg and Sing, 1967).

Most experiments involve adsorption from either the gas phase or from the liquid phase onto a solid surface, and these will be discussed separately.

**Adsorption from the gas phase**

Study of adsorption usually involves determining an adsorption isotherm, that is, plotting the concentration $x$ of adsorbed molecules as a function of their partial pressure $p$ in the gas phase at a given temperature. Adsorption from the gas phase can usually be represented by the BET equation

$$\frac{p}{x(p_0 - p)} = \frac{k}{x_m} + \frac{(1-k)p}{x_m p_0}$$

where $x$ = mass of adsorbate in g per kg adsorbent
$p_0$ = saturation vapour pressure of adsorbate in bar
$k$ is a constant.

Hence by plotting $p/x(p_0 - p)$ against $p/p_0$ it is possible to obtain a straight line from which $x_m$ (and $k$) may be calculated (Gregg and Sing, 1967). In conventional studies, which are carried out at low temperatures, the gas used is generally nitrogen, for which $A = 0{\cdot}162\ nm^2$. Pressures are measured using a McLeod gauge, and the solid sample needs to have a surface area of a few square metres.

Much smaller samples may be used if nitrogen is replaced by krypton labelled with $^{85}Kr$. Krypton-85 is an inert gas with a long half-life (10·6 years) which emits strong betas and weak gamma-radiation. It is available at specific activities of up to 80 mCi $cm^{-3}$ at N.T.P. $A$ for krypton is usually taken as $0{\cdot}208\ nm^2$.

Several techniques have been suggested for its use. Aylmore and Jepson (1961) measured the adsorption of krypton by its decrease in volume, and used the beta-radioactivity of the unabsorbed gas as a measure of its pressure. On the other hand Clarke (1964) measured

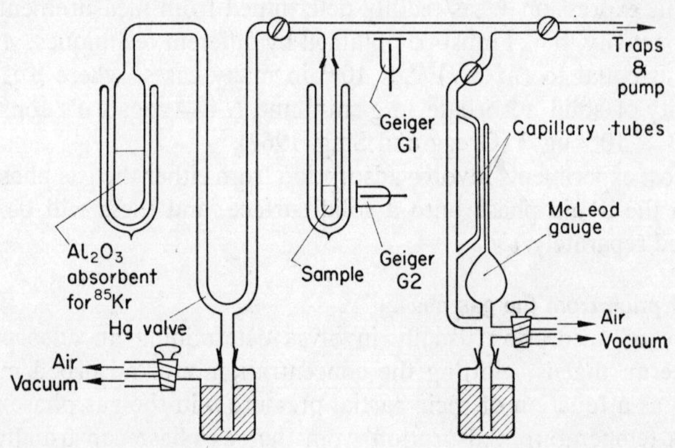


FIG. 7.4. Houtman and Medema's apparatus for determining surface areas of solids by adsorption of krypton-85. G1 measures pressure and gives about $3 \times 10^5$ counts $s^{-1}$ $bar^{-1}$, while G2 measures surface area and gives about 80 counts $s^{-1}$ $m^{-2}$

the pressure with a McLeod gauge and counted the gamma-radiation from the sample which had adsorbed the active krypton. Houtman and Medema (1966) used measurements of beta-activity to determine both pressure and amount adsorbed, and found excellent agreement with conventional techniques using nitrogen. Their apparatus is shown in Fig. 7.4. Other workers have suggested the use of xenon-133 (Chènebault and Schürenkämper, 1965; Cochrane *et al.*, 1967) or carbon monoxide-C14 (Hughes *et al.*, 1962) for surface area measurements. Samples with surface areas as low as 1 $cm^2$ can be used, and the pressures employed may be as low as $10^{-12}$ bar. Hence one can use almost any type of sample, from glass beads with a known geometrical surface area to amorphous solids or powders.

**Adsorption from the liquid phase**

Many workers have studied the uptake of radioactive ions by metal, glass or other surfaces (e.g. Siejka and Campbell, 1958; Hesford *et al.*, 1963; Lieser, 1965; Tingley, 1965; Randall *et al.*, 1965). For example Schwab (1962) has investigated the kinetics of adsorption of $^{82}Br^-$, $^{36}Cl^-$, $^{36}ClO_4^-$, $^{14}CN^-$, $^{18}F^-$, $^{35}SH^-$ and $^{35}SO_4^{2-}$ onto iron, nickel and platinum surfaces. He was able to show that adsorption from solution is an extremely rapid process provided that both the metal surface and the solution are completely free of oxygen. Most experimenters have used metal surfaces on which oxygen atoms are chemisorbed, and these adsorb anions rather slowly, probably by anion exchange with oxide ions. Autoradiography has shown that adsorption occurs preferentially at grain boundaries.

Some particularly interesting studies have been made by making the metal surface an electrode and studying the effects of different voltages on adsorption. For example, Balashova and Kazarinov (1965) have measured the adsorption of both caesium and sulphate ions on a platinum electrode immersed in caesium sulphate solution. When the electrode is negatively charged it is covered with a layer of caesium ions, but these desorb as the electrode is made more and more positive and are replaced by sulphate ions (Fig. 7.5).

Attempts to measure surface areas by adsorption of radioactive ions are not unequivocal. For example, Stow and Spinks (1955) reported measurements of adsorption of both $^{90}Sr^{2+}$ and $^{35}SO_4^{2-}$ on strontium sulphate precipitates. A weighed quantity of strontium sulphate was shaken with a saturated solution of strontium sulphate labelled with one or other radioisotope. The suspension was then centrifuged and the activity of solid and liquid fractions was determined. According to Stow and Spinks, equilibrium was attained after shaking for ten minutes, at which time 55·8% of the strontium but only 35·5% of the sulphate ions had been adsorbed. The

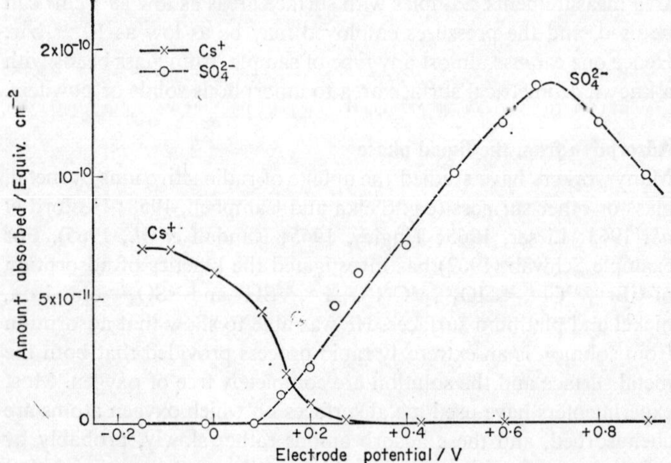


FIG. 7.5. Adsorption of ions from 0·005M $Cs_2SO_4$ + 0·005M $H_2SO_4$ onto a platinum electrode. (After Balashova and Kazarinov, 1965)

apparent surface areas calculated from these data were 1·53 $m^2\ g^{-1}$ and 0·74 $m^2\ g^{-1}$ respectively. It would appear that Stow and Spinks were measuring surface exchange rather than surface adsorption, and that bulk diffusion of one or both ions was taking place.

More reliable measurements of surface areas are obtainable using long-chain molecules labelled with weak beta-emitters. Such molecules frequently form a true monolayer on a wide variety of surfaces, and provided their apparent molecular areas are known, give reproducible values for surface areas. Two techniques have been widely employed, the *Equilibration technique* and the technique of Blomgren and Bockris (1960).

In the *Equilibration technique*, a dilute solution of a long-chain molecule such as stearic acid-1-C14 is employed. This substance is obtainable in specific activities of up to 40 Ci per mole, and is dissolved to form an approximately 0·01M solution in a solvent such as benzene or *n*-hexadecane. The sample whose surface area is required, which may be a massive block or a finely divided powder, is cleaned and dried with care, and should be freed from oxygen by degassing in a vacuum. It is then exposed to the de-oxygenated solution for about one hour, with occasional stirring. The solid and liquid fractions are then separated and their activities determined (Kordecki and Gandy, 1961; Walker and Ries, 1962). The apparent molecular area of stearic acid is taken to be 0·205 nm$^2$. In this way, using samples weighing about 1 g, it is possible to measure surface areas in the range of 0·5–50 m$^2$. The main experimental difficulties are the production of clean surfaces, and the washing of the solid fraction to remove adherent liquid without causing desorption.

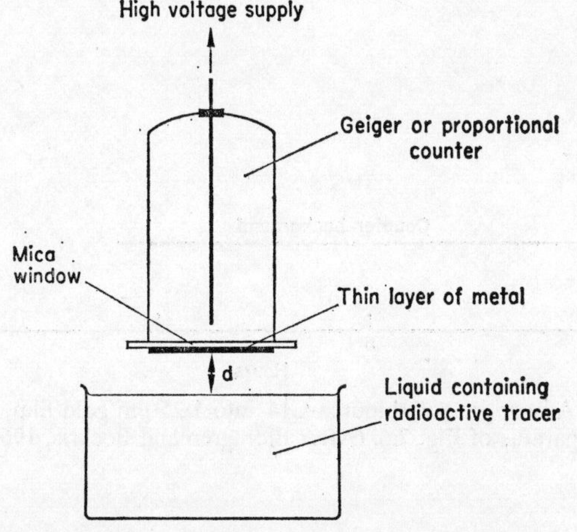


FIG. 7.6. Apparatus for measuring adsorption of molecules from the liquid phase onto thin metal films: the distance *d* is steadily decreased until the metal contacts the surface of the liquid.

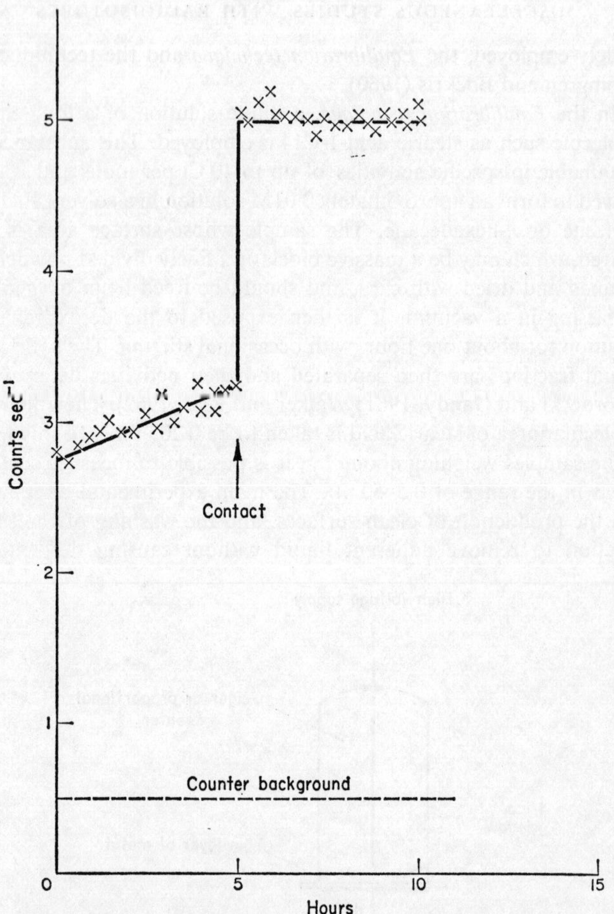


FIG. 7.7. Adsorption of thiourea-C14 into 1·25 μm gold film, using the apparatus of Fig. 7.6. (After Blomgren and Bockris, 1960)

Many labelled substances other than stearic acid have been used, but they do not seem to have any major advantages; e.g. sodium dodecyl sulphate-T (Nilsson, 1957); *n*-nonadecanoic acid 1-C14 (Smith and McGill, 1957); hexadecyl-1-C14trimethyl ammonium bromide (Kivel *et al.*, 1963) and perfluoro-octanoic acid-1-C14 (Shepard and Ryan, 1956 and 1959).

Blomgren and Bockris (1960) apparatus is shown in Fig. 7.6. In their technique a thin layer of metal is deposited on the mica window of a Geiger or Proportional counter. The window is then moved successively closer and closer to a solution containing a radioactive adsorbate emitting weak beta-radiation. The count-rate increases discontinuously at the moment of contact, and the amount of the label adsorbed may be estimated from the magnitude of the observed discontinuity (Fig. 7.7). This technique has mostly been applied to gold films since this metal is readily applied and maintained oxide-free on its mica support. A number of adsorbates have been tested, including benzene-C14 and naphthalene-C14 (Bockris *et al.*, 1964; Dahms and Green, 1963), thiourea (Wroblowa and Green, 1963) *n*-decylamine-1-C14 (Bockris and Swinkels, 1964) and calcium dinonyl naphthalene sulphonate-S35 (Smith *et al.*, 1965).

**Adsorption at the liquid–gas interface**

The adsorption of long-chain molecules, such as detergents, at the water–air interface has been demonstrated by Salley *et al.* (1950) and Aniansson (1951). These authors used detergent molecules labelled with a weak beta-emitter, e.g. sodium hexadecyl sulphate-S35, and compared the activity $a_i$ counts s$^{-1}$ at the interface with the activity $a$ in the bulk solution. The excess detergent adsorbed at the interface $\Gamma$ is given by:

$$\Gamma = \frac{a_i - a}{sA} \text{ mol m}^{-2}$$

where $s$ is the specific activity of an infinitely thin layer of labelled detergent in counts s$^{-1}$ mol$^{-1}$, and $A$ is its surface area in m$^2$.

**Adsorption at the liquid–liquid interface**

Bresee and Chester (1958) have shown that the interfacial area between two immiscible liquids may be measured using the ($\alpha$, $n$)

reaction. 200 mCi of $^{210}Po(NO_3)_4$, which emits alpha-particles with a short range, was dissolved in water and shaken with perfluoro-*n*-heptane. Neutrons were formed at the interface by the reaction

$$^{19}F(\alpha, n)^{23}Na$$

in numbers proportional to the interfacial area, but the detection of these neutrons involved considerable problems. The reaction was carried out in a 1·5 m diameter sphere of pure graphite containing eight boron trifluoride neutron counters. The method is interesting but has not been developed further.

**Electrodeposition**

Techniques applied in surface area studies can also be used to follow the rates of electrodeposition. For example, Doty and Riley (1967) have studied the kinetics of the electrodeposition of metallic nickel. Madi (1962, 1964, 1966) has measured the rates of deposition of silver, thallium, lead, manganese and lanthanide cations from dilute nitric acid onto platinum anodes. It appears that the cations involved are attracted to an oxide layer on the anode when they are present at concentrations of about $10^{-8}$M. Tudor *et al.* (1965) have investigated the breakdown of lead accumulators after many charge–discharge cycles. The electrolyte was labelled with $H_2{}^{35}SO_4$, and autoradiography demonstrated that breakdown was caused by the deposition of a layer of lead sulphate on the electrodes. The deposition of antimony-124 in the lead accumulator has been studied by Herrmann and Pröpstl (1957).

**Corrosion**

Radiochemical methods have been useful in the study of corrosion. In early work, Bardeen *et al.* (1946) electrodeposited a thin layer of $^{64}Cu$ onto a copper plate. The plate was then heated to 1000°C in air, cooled, and the oxide layer was dissolved off by repeated exposure to nitric acid. The loss in weight after each exposure was compared with the radioactivity in the solution, so that the thickness of the oxide layer and its composition could be calculated. Later workers have used hetero-atoms to label the surfaces of metals exposed to oxidation, e.g. silver-110 on molybdenum (Simnad and Spilness, 1955).

Corrosion by aqueous solutions is of great technical importance. Neither exchange nor corrosion takes place for several hours when a clean metal surface is exposed to oxygen-free solutions containing a radiotracer, at least if the metal is iron (Lieser *et al.*, 1964) or zinc (Lieser and Bachmann, 1964). If oxygen is present, corrosion takes place, and can be studied using autoradiography. The region of maximum corrosion coincides with the region of maximum exchange with the tracer from the solution, which is usually at the metal/solution/air junction. Autoradiographic techniques demonstrate that corrosion occurs before the corrosion products are detectable chemically. For example, zinc immersed in 0·001M zinc chloride for ten minutes shows no detectable change, but if the zinc chloride is labelled with $^{65}Zn$, pitting of the metal surface can be clearly seen on autoradiographs.

Davies and co-workers (1962, 1963) have used a novel technique to investigate anodic oxidation in aluminium and tantalum. These metal surfaces are normally coated with an oxide layer which steadily grows in thickness during electrolysis. In order to test whether growth occurs at the surface of the oxide layer, or at the metal/oxide interface, the anode surface was labelled with an inert alpha-emitter ($^{222}Rn$) or a very weak beta-emitter ($^{125}Xe$). After anodic oxidation it was found that the radon label was partially buried but retained its well-defined distribution: experiments with the xenon label were less conclusive.

### Heterogeneous catalysis

The applications of radioactive tracers to problems in catalysis fall into three classes: the use of labelled catalysts, the determination of surface areas of catalysts using labelled molecules, and the study of reactions of labelled molecules over unlabelled catalysts. Care should be taken to distinguish between the radioactivity and catalytic activity of catalysts when discussing them.

The use of labelled catalysts to measure the mechanical attrition of valuable catalysts such as iridium gauze has already been described (Chapter 2). Unfortunately it has not proved possible to use radioactive labelling to determine the valency state of atoms in catalysts, though Mössbauer studies may enable this to be done.

Radioactive catalysts may increase catalytic efficiency somewhat. Balandin and Spitzyn (1961) claimed that the catalytic activity of labelled sodium sulphate, magnesium sulphate and calcium phosphate in the dehydration of isopropanol or cyclohexanol increased with the specific radioactivity, while the activation energies decreased by 0·04–0·08 eV.

The surface areas of catalysts may be determined by the methods described earlier in this chapter, using krypton-85 or xenon-133. These methods fail for the important class of supported catalysts, such as platinized asbestos or 5% platinum on alumina, because they give the total area of metal plus support. Hughes *et al.* (1962) have shown that carbon monoxide-C14 can be used to measure the surface area of platinum metals in the presence of inert supports, since this gas is not appreciably absorbed by alumina at temperatures where the metal forms a complete monolayer. They passed helium containing 0·5 mol % labelled carbon monoxide over the supported catalyst at a known flow-rate, and measured the radioactivity of the gas stream before and after adsorption. The volume of gas adsorbed is given by

$$V_{ads} = \frac{273pfx_0}{T}\left(t - \frac{c}{a_0}\right) \text{ m}^3$$

where $p$ = pressure in bars, $T$ = temperature in K, $f$ = flow-rate in $m^3 s^{-1}$, $x_0$ = mole fraction of CO before adsorption, $t$ = time period of run in seconds, $c$ = total count from gas stream after adsorption, $a_0$ = counts per second from gas stream before adsorption. There is a small correction for dead space occupied by the catalyst.

There is no reason why other radioactive gases should not be substituted for carbon monoxide, and indeed both $^{203}Hg$ (Affrossman and Erskine, 1966) and ethylene-C14 (Cormack *et al.*, 1966) have been used for similar experiments.

Among the large number of investigations of reactions of labelled molecules with or over heterogeneous catalysts, the best known is perhaps the work on the Fischer–Tropsch synthesis of hydrocarbons from carbon monoxide and hydrogen over iron and cobalt oxides. Studies with $^{14}CO$ and labelled cobalt carbide proved that metallic carbides were not involved in the synthesis (Emmett, 1957). The intermediate complex formed probably resembles adsorbed ketene (Blyholder and Emmett, 1959). Other investigations include the hydrogenation of ethylene-C14 over nickel (Thomson and Wishlade, 1962) the hydrogenation of crotonic acid-C14 and vinylacetic acid-C14 over palladized barium sulphate (Affrossman *et al.*, 1962), the oxidation of carbon monoxide-C14 over manganese dioxide (Klier and Kuchynka,1966), the oxidation of perfluoropropylene-F18 over alkali metal fluorides (Wethington *et al.*, 1958) and the isomerization of ethyl cyclohexane-C14 over nickel/alumina (Pines and Shaw, 1957).

The heterogeneity of catalyst surfaces can be demonstrated by adsorbing a radioactive gas G* and then displacing it by exchange with inactive G at a range of temperatures. In general the specific activity desorbed varies with temperature, showing that G is more firmly bound to some parts of the surface than to others. Heterogeneity of a nickel surface has thus been demonstrated using tritium (Cranstoun and Thomson, 1963), acetylene-C14 (Keier, 1952) and ethylene-C14 (Thomson and Wishlade, 1962) as well as for platinum using gaseous mercury-203 (Affrossman and Erskine, 1966).

## References

AFFROSSMAN, S., CORMACK, D., and THOMSON, S. J. (1962). *J. Chem. Soc.*, 3217.

AFFROSSMAN, S., and ERSKINE, W. G. (1966). *Trans. Faraday Soc.*, **62,** 2922.

ANIANSSON, G. (1951). *J. Phys. Colloid Chem.*, **55,** 1286.

AYLMORE, D. W., and JEPSON, W. B. (1961). *J. Scient. Instrum.*, **38,** 156.

BALANDIN, A. A., and SPITZYN, V. I. (1961). *Dokl. Akad. Nauk S.S.S.R.*, **137,** 627.

BALASHOVA, N. A., and KAZARINOV, V. E. (1965). *Russ. Chem. Revs.*, **34,** 730.

BARDEEN, J., BRATTAIN, W. H., and SHOCKLEY, W. (1946). *J. Chem. Phys.*, **14,** 714.

BLOMGREN, E. A., and BOCKRIS, J. O'M. (1960). *Nature, Lond.*, **186,** 305.

BLYHOLDER, G., and EMMETT, P. H. (1959). *J. Phys. Chem.*, **63,** 962.

BOCKRIS, J. O'M., GREEN, M., and SWINKELS, D. A. J. (1964). *J. Electrochem. Soc.*, **111,** 743.

BOCKRIS, J. O'M., and SWINKELS, D. A. J. (1964). *J. Electrochem. Soc.*, **111,** 736.

BOYD, G. A. (1955). *Autoradiography in Biology and Medicine.* Academic Press.

BRESEE, J. C., and CHESTER, C. V. (1958). *Proc. Int. Conf. Peaceful Uses of Atomic Energy*, **20,** 158, New York.

CHAMBERLAIN, J., HUGHES, A., ROGERS, A. W., and THOMAS, G. H. (1964). *Nature, Lond.*, **201,** 774.

CHÈNEBAULT, P., and SCHÜRENKÄMPER, A. (1965). *J. Phys. Chem.*, **69,** 2300.

CLARKE, J. T. (1964). *J. Phys. Chem.*, **68,** 884.

COCHRANE, H., WALKER, P. L., DIETHORN, W. S., and FRIEDMAN, H. C. (1967). *J. Colloid Interface Sci.*, **24,** 405.

COOK, G. B., and PROUT, E W. (1956). *J. Inorg. Nucl. Chem.*, **3,** 255.

CORMACK, D., THOMSON, S. J., and WEBB, G. (1966). *J. Catalysis*, **5,** 224.

CRANSTOUN, G. K. L., and THOMSON, S. J. (1963). *Trans. Faraday Soc.*, **59,** 2403.

DAHMS, H., and GREEN, M. (1963). *J. Electrochem. Soc.*, **110,** 1075.

DAVIES, J. A., and DOMEIJ, B. (1963). *J. Electrochem. Soc.*, **110,** 849.

DAVIES, J. A., PRINGLE, J. P. S., GRAHAM, R. L., and BROWN, F. (1962). *J. Electrochem. Soc.*, **109,** 999.

DOTY, W. R., and RILEY, B. J. (1967). *J. Electrochem. Soc.*, **114,** 50.

EMMETT, P. H. (1957). *Adv. Catalysis*, **9,** 645.

FAIRES, R. A., and PARKS, B. H. (1964). *Radioisotope Laboratory Techniques*, 2nd ed. Newnes.

FALK, G. J., and KING, R. C. (1963). *Radiat. Res.*, **20,** 466.

GREGG, S. J., and SING, K. S. W. (1967). *Adsorption, Surface Area and Porosity.* Academic Press.

HAHN, O., and MÜLLER, O. (1923). *Z. Elektrochem.*, **29,** 189.

HERRMANN, W., and PRÖPSTL, G. (1957). *Z. Elektrochem.*, **61,** 1154.

HERZ, R. H. (1951). *Nucleonics*, **9,** no. 3, 24.

HESFORD, E., WILLIAMS, J., and WALTON, G. N. (1963). *Radiochim. Acta*, **2,** 14.

HOUTMAN, J. P. W., and MEDEMA, J. (1966). *Ber. Bunsen. Phys. Chem.*, **70,** 489.

HUGHES, T. R., HOUSTON, R. J., and SIEG, R. P. (1962). *Ind. Engng. Chem. Proc. Design Dev.*, **1,** 96.

JECH, C. (1960). *Int. J. Appl. Radiat. Isotopes*, **8,** 179.

KAISER, H. (1954). *Z. Elektrochem.*, **58,** 601.

KEIER, N. P. (1952). *Izv. Akad. Nauk S.S.S.R. Otd. Khim. Nauk*, 616.

KIVEL, J., ALBERS, F. C., OLSEN, D. A., and JOHNSON, R. E. (1963). *J. Phys. Chem.*, **67,** 1235.

KLIER, K., and KUCHYNKA, K. (1966). *J. Catalysis*, **6,** 62.

KORDECKI, M. C., and GANDY, M. B. (1961). *Int. J. Appl. Radiat. Isotopes*, **12,** 27.

LIESER, K. H. (1965). *Radiochim. Acta*, **4,** 225.

LIESER, K. H., and BACHMANN, K. (1964). *Corrosion Sci.*, **4,** 63.

LIESER, K. H., KALVANES, O., and COMPOSTELLA, S. (1964). *Corrosion Sci.*, **4,** 51.

MADI, I. (1962). *J. Inorg. Nucl. Chem.*, **24,** 1501.

MADI, I. (1964). *J. Inorg. Nucl. Chem.*, **26,** 2135 and 2149.

MADI, I. (1966). *J. Inorg. Nucl. Chem.*, **28,** 335.

MOYER, J. D., and OCHS, R. J. (1963). *Science, N.Y.*, **142,** 1316.

NILSSON, G. (1957). *J. Phys. Chem.*, **61,** 1135.

PINES, H., and SHAW, A. W. (1957). *Adv. Catalysis*, **9,** 569.

PURKAYASTHA, B. C., and SARKAR, S. (1966). *J. Inorg. Nucl. Chem.*, **28,** 347.

RANDALL, J. J., BERNARD, W. J., and WILKINSON, R. R. (1965). *Electrochim. Acta*, **10,** 183.

ROGERS, A. W. (1967). *Techniques of Autoradiography*. Elsevier.

SALLEY, D. J., WEITH, A. J., ARGYLE, A. A., and DIXON, J. K. (1950). *Proc. Roy. Soc. A*, **203,** 42.

SCHWABE, K. (1962). *Electrochim. Acta*, **6,** 223.

SHABOWRA, G., and SCHIBANOWA, M. D. (1965). *Reactivity of Solids*, edited by Schwab, G. M., p. 52. Elsevier.

SHEPARD, J. W., and RYAN, J. P. (1956). *J. Phys. Chem.*, **60,** 127.

SHEPARD, J. W., and RYAN, J. P. (1959). *J. Phys. Chem.*, **63,** 1729.

SIEJKA, L., and CAMPBELL, I. G. (1958). *Proc. Int. Conf. on Peaceful Uses of Atomic Energy*, **20,** 148, New York.

SIMNAD, M. T., and SPILNESS, A. (1955). *Trans. Amer. Inst. Min. Metall. Engr.*, **203,** 1011.

SMITH, H. A., and MCGILL, R. M. (1957). *J. Phys. Chem.*, **61,** 1025.

SMITH, M. L., GORDON, B. E., and NELSON, R. C. (1965). *J. Phys. Chem.*, **69,** 3833.

STOW, R. M., and SPINKS, J. W. T. (1955). *Can. J. Chem.*, **33,** 938.

TAYLOR, J. H. (1960). *Adv. Biol. Med. Phys.*, **7,** 107.

THOMSON, S. J., and WISHLADE, J. L. (1962). *Trans. Faraday Soc.*, **58,** 1170.

TINGLEY, I. I. (1965). *J. Electrochem. Soc.*, **112,** 60.

TUDOR, S., WEISSTUCH, A., and DAVANG, S. H. (1965). *Electrochem. Technol.*, **3,** 90.

ULLBERG, S. (1965). *Isotopes in Experimental Pharmacology*, edited by Stumpf, W. E., and Roth, L. J., p. 145. Academic Press.

WALKER, D. C., and RIES, H. E. (1962). *J. Colloid Sci.*, **17,** 789.

WARD, R. G. (1960). *The Physical Examination of Metals*, edited by Chalmers, B., and Quarrell, A. G., 2nd ed., p. 825. Arnold.

WETHINGTON, J. A., GENS, T. A., CHRISTIE, W. H., and BROSI, A. R. (1958). *Proc. Int. Conf. on Peaceful Uses of Atomic Energy*, **20**, 132, New York.

WROBLOWA, H., and GREEN, M. (1963). *Electrochim. Acta*, **8**, 679.

# Appendix 1

*Table of Half-lives of Common Radionuclides, together with their main radiations and radiation energies.*

| Nuclide | Half-life | Main α-energies /MeV | Maximum β-energies /MeV | Main γ-energies /MeV | Max. spec. activity /Ci $g^{-1}$ | Notes |
|---|---|---|---|---|---|---|
| Actinium-227 | 22 yr | 4·94 | 0·04 | — | 70 | |
| Aluminium-26 | $7{\cdot}4 \times 10^5$ yr | — | — | 0·51, 1·83 | 0·019 | |
| Aluminium-28 | 2·3 min | — | 2·87 | 1·78 | 0·13 | |
| Americium-241 | 458 yr | 5·4, 5·5 | — | 0·03, 0·06 | 3 | active daughters |
| Antimony-122 | 2·7 d | — | 1·42, 1·99 | 0·57 | 0·52 | |
| Antimony-124 | 60 d | — | 0·61, 2·31 | 0·60, 1·70 | 0·14 | |
| Argon-41 | 110 min | — | 1·20 | 1·29 | 0·2 | |
| Arsenic-73 | 76 d | — | — | <0·01 | 24000 | $^{73}$Ge daughter |
| Arsenic-74 | 18 d | — | 0·72, 1·36 | 0·51, 0·60 | 10 | |
| Arsenic-76 | 26 hr | — | 2·41, 2·97 | 0·56 | 0·9 | |
| Barium-131 | 11·5 d | — | — | 0·50 | 0·001 | $^{131}$Cs daughter |
| Barium-133 | 7·5 yr | — | — | 0·08, 0·36 | 1 | |
| Barium-140 | 12·8 d | — | 1·02 | 0·16, 0·54 | 90,000 | $^{140}$La daughter |
| Beryllium-7 | 53 d | — | — | 0·48 | 350,000 | |
| Bismuth-210 | 5·0 d | 5·06 | 1·17 | — | 0·0015 | $^{210}$Po daughter |
| Bismuth-212 | 1 hr | 6·1 | 1·55, 2·25 | 0·73 | $1{\cdot}5 \times 10^7$ | |

| Nuclide | Half-life | Main α-energies /MeV | Maximum β-energies /MeV | Main γ-energies /MeV | Max. spec. activity /Ci $g^{-1}$ | Notes |
|---|---|---|---|---|---|---|
| Bromine-80 | 18 min | — | 1·38, 2·02 | 0·51, 0·62 | 1·2 | |
| Bromine-82 | 36 hr | — | 0·44 | 0·55, 0·78 | 0·3 | |
| Bromine-88 | 16 s | — | + | — | $8 \times 10^{9}$ | *n*-emitter |
| Bromine-90 | 1·6 s | — | + | — | $8 \times 10^{10}$ | *n*-emitter |
| Cadmium-109 | 470 d | — | — | 0·088 | 2500 | |
| Cadmium-115m | 43 d | — | 1·11, 1·61 | 0·34, 0·52 | 0·006 | |
| Caesium-134 | 2·2 yr | — | 0·65 | 0·61, 0·80 | 3·5 | |
| Caesium-137 | 30 yr | — | 0·51 | 0·66 | 90 | |
| Calcium-45 | 165 d | — | 0·25 | — | 0·006 | |
| Calcium-47 | 4·7 d | — | 0·66 | 1·31 | 0·000003 | $^{47}Sc$ daughter |
| Calcium-49 | 8·8 min | — | 0·89, 2·0 | 3·1, 4·1, 4·7 | 0·0014 | $^{49}Sc$ daughter |
| Carbon-14 | 5760 yr | — | 0·155 | — | 2·7 | |
| Cerium-139 | 140 d | — | — | 0·10, 0·17 | 7000 | |
| Cerium-141 | 32·5 d | — | 0·44, 0·58 | 0·15 | 0·03 | |
| Cerium-144 | 285 d | — | 0·32, 2·98 | 0·13, 0·69 | 3000 | $^{144}Pr$ daughter |
| Chlorine-36 | 30,000 yr | — | 0·71 | — | 0·0005 | |
| Chlorine-38 | 37 min | — | 1·11, 4·81 | 1·60, 2·15 | 0·06 | |
| Chromium-51 | 28 d | — | — | 0·32 | 0·02 | |
| Cobalt-57 | 270 d | — | — | 0·12 | 8000 | |
| Cobalt-58 | 71 d | — | — | 0·51, 0·81 | 32,000 | |
| Cobalt-60 | 5·3 yr | — | 0·31 | 1·17, 1·33 | 10 | |
| Copper-64 | 13 hr | — | 0·57 | 0·51 | 0·7 | |
| Dysprosium-165 | 2·3 hr | — | 1·31 | 0·10, 0·36 | 80 | |
| Erbium-171 | 7·5 hr | — | 1·10 | 0·11, 0·30 | 0·1 | $^{171}Tm$ daughter |

| | | | | | | |
|---|---|---|---|---|---|---|
| Europium-152 | 13 yr | — | 0·71 | 0·12, 1·41 | 70 | |
| Fluorine-18 | 112 min | — | — | 0·51 | $9 \times 10^7$ | |
| Gadolinium-153 | 236 d | — | — | 0·10 | 0·03 | |
| Gallium-72 | 14 hr | — | 0·67, 0·96 | 0·83, 2·20 | 0·5 | |
| Germanium-71 | 11 d | — | — | 0·0092 | 0·016 | |
| Germanium-73m | 0·53 s | — | — | 0·014, 0·054 | $3 \times 10^{11}$ | |
| Germanium-77 | 11 hr | — | 1·56, 2·12 | 0·21, 0·42 | 0·0015 | |
| Gold-198 | 2·7 d | — | 0·96 | 0·41 | 8 | |
| Hafnium-181 | 42·5 d | — | 0·41 | 0·13, 0·48 | 0·32 | |
| Holmium-166 | 27 hr | — | 1·84 | 0·08 | 6 | |
| Hydrogen-3 | 12·3 yr | — | 0·018 | — | 10,000 | |
| Indium-114m | 50 d | — | 1·98 | 0·19 | 0·3 | $^{114}In$ daughter |
| Indium-116m | 54 min | — | 1·00 | 1·09, 1·27 | 20 | |
| Iodine-125 | 60 d | — | — | 0·035 | 0·4 | |
| Iodine-128 | 25 min | — | 1·67, 2·12 | 0·45 | 0·72 | |
| Iodine-131 | 8·0 d | — | 0·61 | 0·36 | 95,000 | |
| Iodine-132 | 2·3 hr | — | 2·12 | 0·67, 0·78 | $10^7$ | |
| Iridium-192 | 74 d | — | 0·54, 0·67 | 0·31, 0·47 | 32 | |
| Iridium-194 | 19 hr | — | 2·24 | 0·33 | 7 | |
| Iron-55 | 2·7 yr | — | — | 0·0059 | 0·04 | |
| Iron-59 | 45 d | — | 0·27, 0·46 | 1·10, 1·29 | 0·001 | |
| Krypton-85 | 10·6 yr | — | 0·67 | 0·51 | 20 | |
| Lanthanum-140 | 40 hr | — | 1·38 | 0·49, 1·60 | 0·9 | |
| Lead-210 | 21 yr | — | 0·017 | 0·047 | 0·05 | |
| Lead-212 | 11 hr | — | 0·34, 0·58 | 0·24, 0·30 | $1·4 \times 10^6$ | |
| Lutetium-177 | 6·7 d | — | 0·50 | 0·21 | 9 | |
| Magnesium-28 | 21 hr | — | 0·42 | 0·032, 1·35 | 1 | $^{28}Al$ daughter |
| Manganese-54 | 291 d | — | — | 0·84 | 8000 | |
| Manganese-56 | 2·6 hr | — | 2·86 | 0·84, 1·81 | 4 | |

| Nuclide | Half-life | Main $\alpha$-energies /MeV | Maximum $\beta$-energies /MeV | Main $\gamma$-energies /MeV | Max. spec. activity /Ci $g^{-1}$ | Notes |
|---|---|---|---|---|---|---|
| Mercury-197 | 65 hr | — | — | 0·08, 0·13 | 0·35 | |
| Mercury-203 | 47 d | — | 0·21 | 0·28 | 0·09 | |
| Molybdenum-99 | 67 hr | — | 1·23 | 0·14 | 0·015 | $^{99}$Tc daughter |
| Neodymium-147 | 11 d | — | 0·81 | 0·09, 0·53 | 0·3 | $^{147}$Pm daughter |
| Neptunium-239 | 2·3 d | — | 0·33, 0·44 | 0·11, 0·28 | 240,000 | |
| Nickel-63 | 125 yr | — | 0·067 | — | 0·0002 | |
| Nickel-65 | 2·6 hr | — | 2·10 | 1·11, 1·49 | 0·004 | |
| Niobium-95 | 35 d | — | 0·16 | 0·76 | 40,000 | |
| Osmium-191 | 15 d | — | 0·14 | 0·13 | 0·2 | |
| Palladium-109 | 14 hr | — | 1·03 | 0·088 | 0·4 | |
| Phosphorus-32 | 14·2 d | — | 1·71 | — | <300,000 | |
| Platinum-197 | 20 hr | — | 0·67 | 0·077 | 0·02 | |
| Plutonium-238 | 86 yr | 4·4, 5·5 | — | 0·044 | 17 | active daughters |
| Plutonium-239 | 24,400 yr | 5·1 | — | — | 0·06 | $^{239}$Np daughter |
| Polonium-210 | 138 d | 5·3 | — | — | 5400 | |
| Potassium-40 | $1·3 \times 10^9$ yr | — | 1·32 | 1·46 | 0·0018 | |
| Potassium-42 | 12 hr | — | 3·6 | 1·52 | 0·03 | |
| Praseodymium-142 | 19 hr | — | 2·15 | 1·57 | 1 | |
| Promethium-147 | 2·6 yr | — | 0·22 | — | 900 | |
| Protoactinium-233 | 27 d | — | 0·26 | 0·31 | 20,000 | |
| Radium-226 | 1620 yr | 4·6, 4·8 | — | 0·19 | 1 | active daughters |
| Radon-222 | 3·8 d | 5·5 | — | — | 150,000 | active daughters |
| Rhenium-186 | 3·7 d | — | 1·07 | 0·14 | 4 | |
| Rhenium-188 | 17 hr | — | 2·12 | 0·16 | 3·5 | |

| | | | | | | |
|---|---|---|---|---|---|---|
| Rhodium-105 | 1·5 d | — | 0·56 | 0·31 | 800,000 | |
| Rubidium-86 | 19 d | — | 1·77 | 1·08 | 0·15 | |
| Ruthenium-103 | 40 d | — | 0·21 | 0·50 | 0·07 | |
| Ruthenium-106 | 1·0 yr | — | 0·04, 3·6 | 0·51, 0·62 | 3000 | $^{106}$Rh daughter |
| Samarium-153 | 47 hr | — | 0·70 | 0·10 | 4 | |
| Scandium-46 | 84 d | — | 0·36 | 0·89, 1·12 | 8 | |
| Scandium-49 | 58 min | — | 2·05 | — | $7 \times 10^7$ | |
| Selenium-75 | 121 d | — | — | 0·14, 0·27 | 0·05 | |
| Silicon-31 | 2·6 hr | — | 1·47 | — | 0·002 | |
| Silver-110m | 253 d | — | 0·09, 0·53 | 0·66, 0·88 | 0·24 | |
| Sodium-22 | 2·6 yr | — | — | 0·51, 1·28 | $<1$ | |
| Sodium-24 | 15 hr | — | 1·39 | 1·37, 2·75 | 0·39 | |
| Strontium-85 | 65 d | — | — | 0·51 | 4 | |
| Strontium-89 | 51 d | — | 1·46 | — | $<30,000$ | |
| Strontium-90 | 28 yr | — | 0·54 | — | $<140$ | $^{90}$Y daughter |
| Sulphur-35 | 87 d | — | 0·17 | — | 30 | |
| Tantalum-182 | 115 d | — | 0·18, 0·44 | 1·12, 1·22 | 2 | |
| Technetium-99 | 21,200 yr | — | 0·29 | — | 0·2 | |
| Tellurium-127 | 105 d | — | 0·70 | — | 0·02 | |
| Tellurium-132 | 3·25 d | — | 0·22 | 0·23 | 300,000 | $^{132}$I daughter |
| Terbium-160 | 73 d | — | 0·56, 0·86 | 0·30, 0·88 | 2 | |
| Thallium-204 | 3·9 yr | — | 0·77 | — | 0·2 | |
| Thallium-208 | 3·1 min | — | 1·80 | 0·58, 2·61 | $3 \times 10^8$ | |
| Thorium-228 | 1·9 yr | 5·2, 5·4 | — | 0·084 | 800 | active daughters |
| Thorium-232 | $1·4 \times 10^{10}$ yr | 3·9, 4·0 | — | — | $10^{-7}$ | active daughters |
| Thorium-234 | 24 d | — | 0·10, 0·19 | 0·06, 0·09 | 24,000 | |
| Thulium-170 | 127 d | — | 0·97 | 0·084 | 13 | |
| Tin-113 | 119 d | — | — | 0·39 | 0·002 | |
| Tungsten-185 | 73 d | — | 0·43 | — | 0·06 | |

| Nuclide | Half-life | Main $\alpha$-energies /MeV | Maximum $\beta$-energies /MeV | Main $\gamma$-energies /MeV | Max. spec. activity /Ci $g^{-1}$ | Notes |
|---|---|---|---|---|---|---|
| Uranium-235 | $7 \cdot 1 \times 10^8$ yr | 4·2, 4·4 | — | 0·14, 0·19 | $2 \times 10^{-6}$ | active daughters |
| Uranium-238 | $4 \cdot 5 \times 10^9$ yr | 4·2 | — | — | $3 \cdot 3 \times 10^{-7}$ | active daughters |
| Vanadium-48 | 16 d | — | — | 0·99, 1·31 | 170,000 | |
| Xenon-133 | 5·3 d | — | 0·34 | 0·081 | 0·2 | |
| Ytterbium-175 | 4·2 d | — | 0·47 | 0·40 | 1·8 | |
| Yttrium-90 | 64 hr | — | 2·25 | — | 0·23 | |
| Zinc-65 | 245 d | — | — | 1·11 | 0·05 | |
| Zinc-69 | 14 hr | — | 0·91 | 0·44 | 0·005 | |
| Zirconium-95 | 65 d | — | 0·40 | 0·73, 0·76 | 20,000 | $^{95}$Nb daughter |

For further information, including a fuller listing of all the beta- and gamma-energies, see Allen, R. A., Smith, D. B., and Hiscott, J. E., A. E.R.E.-R 2938 (1961): H.M.S.O., London; and the Nuclear Data sheets of the National Academy of Sciences, National Research Council, Washington D.C.

Most of the maximum specific activities were calculated theoretically and experimentally obtainable specific activities may be many orders of magnitude lower: for nuclides produced by activation with thermal neutrons, a flux of $10^{16}$ neutrons $m^{-2}$ $s^{-1}$ was assumed.

# Appendix 2

*Physical Constants and Units*

| | | |
|---|---|---|
| Avogadro constant | $N$ | $6{\cdot}0225 \times 10^{23}$ mol$^{-1}$ |
| Boltzmann constant | $k$ | $1{\cdot}3805 \times 10^{-23}$ J K$^{-1}$<br>$8{\cdot}617 \times 10^{-5}$ eV K$^{-1}$ |
| Faraday constant | $F$ | $9{\cdot}6487 \times 10^{4}$ C mol$^{-1}$ |
| Gas constant | $R$ | $8{\cdot}314$ J K$^{-1}$ mol$^{-1}$ |
| Planck constant | $h$ | $6{\cdot}6256 \times 10^{-34}$ J s$^{-1}$ |
| Proton charge | $e$ | $1{\cdot}6021 \times 10^{-19}$ C |
| Electron mass | $m_e$ | $9{\cdot}1091 \times 10^{-31}$ kg |
| Neutron mass | $m_n$ | $1{\cdot}67482 \times 10^{-27}$ kg |
| Proton mass | $m_p$ | $1{\cdot}67252 \times 10^{-27}$ kg |
| Velocity of light | $c$ | $2{\cdot}997925 \times 10^{8}$ m s$^{-1}$ |
| 1 day | | $8{\cdot}64 \times 10^{4}$ s |
| 1 year | | $3{\cdot}15569 \times 10^{7}$ s |
| 1 Curie | | $3{\cdot}7 \times 10^{10}$ disintegrations s$^{-1}$ |
| 1 u | | $1{\cdot}6604 \times 10^{-27}$ kg |
| 1 eV | | $1{\cdot}6021 \times 10^{-19}$ J |
| 1 bar | | $10^{5}$ N m$^{-2}$ |
| Ice melts at | | $273{\cdot}150$ K |

# Appendi

*Table of Beta-particle ener*

| β-energy /MeV \ Half-life | <1 hr | 1–6 hr | 6–24 hr |
|---|---|---|---|
| 0·01–0·02 | | | |
| 0·02–0·05 | | | |
| 0·05–0·10 | | | |
| 0·10–0·20 | | | |
| 0·20–0·50 | | | |
| 0·50–0·75 | | | $^{64}$Cu, $^{72}$Ga, $^{197}$Pt |
| 0·75–1·00 | | | $^{69}$Zn, $^{72}$Ga, $^{159}$Gd |
| 1·00–1·50 | $^{38}$Cl $^{81}$Se | *$^{31}$Si*, $^{41}$Ar, $^{97}$Nb, $^{105}$Ru | $^{24}$Na, $^{109}$Pd, $^{171}$Er |
| 1·50–2·00 | $^{70}$Ga, $^{80}$Br | $^{149}$Nd | $^{97}$Zr |
| 2·00–5·00 | $^{28}$Al, $^{38}$Cl, $^{106}$Rh, $^{144}$Pr | $^{56}$Mn, $^{65}$Ni, $^{139}$Ba | $^{42}$K, $^{142}$Pr, $^{188}$Re, $^{194}$Ir |

N.B. Pure beta-emitters are printed in *italics*.

*Half-lives of nuclides*

| 1–5 d | 5–30 d | 30 d–1 yr | >1 yr |
|---|---|---|---|
| | | | $^{3}\mathit{H}$, $^{210}Pb$ |
| | | $^{141}Ce$ | $^{106}Ru$ |
| | | | $^{63}\mathit{Ni}$, $^{134}Cs$ |
| | $^{191}Os$ | $^{35}\mathit{S}$, $^{95}Nb$, $^{203}Hg$ | $^{14}\mathit{C}$, $^{155}Eu$ |
| Br, $^{121}\mathit{Sn}$, $^{175}Yb$ | $^{133}Xe$, $^{169}\mathit{Er}$, $^{177}Yb$ | $^{45}\mathit{Ca}$, $^{46}Sc$, $^{59}Fe$, $^{95}Zr$, $^{103}$ Ru, $^{144}Ce$, $^{181}Hf$, $^{185}W$ | $^{60}Co$, $^{87}\mathit{Rb}$, $^{99}\mathit{Tc}$, $^{147}\mathit{Pm}$ |
| $^{5}Rh$, $^{187}W$ | $^{131}I$ | $^{124}Sb$, $^{182}Ta$, $^{192}Ir$ | $^{36}\mathit{Cl}$, $^{85}Kr$, $^{90}\mathit{Sr}$, $^{134}Cs$, $^{137}Cs$ |
| $^{3}Au$ | $^{143}\mathit{Pr}$, $^{160}Tb$ | $^{170}Tm$ | $^{204}\mathit{Tl}$ |
| Mo, $^{143}Ce$, $^{149}Pm$, $^{186}Re$, $^{193}Os$ | $^{210}\mathit{Bi}$ | $^{89}\mathit{Sr}$ | |
| $^{2}Sb$, $^{166}Ho$ | $^{32}\mathit{P}$, $^{86}Rb$ | $^{91}Y$, $^{114}In$ | |
| As, $^{90}\mathit{Y}$ | | $^{124}Sb$ | |

# Appendi

*Table of X-ray and Gamma-ene*

| Half-life / γ-energy /MeV | <1 hr | 1–6 hr | 6–24 hr |
|---|---|---|---|
| <0·01 | | $^{180m}$Hf | $^{64}$Cu |
| 0·01–0·02 | $^{94m}$Nb | $^{87m}$Sr | $^{137}$Ce |
| 0·02–0·05 | $^{51}$Ti, $^{94m}$Nb | $^{80m}$Br, $^{134m}$Cs | $^{28}$Mg, $^{109}$Pd |
| 0·05–0·10 | $^{239}$U | $^{176m}$Lu, $^{180m}$Ho | $^{109}$Pd, $^{197}$Pt |
| 0·10–0·20 | | $^{139}$Ba | $^{52}$Fe, $^{188}$Re |
| 0·20–0·50 | | $^{87m}$Sr | $^{69}$Zn, $^{171}$Er |
| 0·50–1·00 | $^{27}$Mg, $^{80}$Br, $^{106}$Rh | $^{56}$Mn, $^{105}$Ru, $^{132}$I | $^{72}$Ga, $^{97}$Zr |
| 1·00–2·00 | $^{28}$Al, $^{38}$Cl, $^{52}$V, $^{116}$In | $^{41}$Ar, $^{56}$Mn, $^{65}$Ni | $^{24}$Na, $^{28}$Mg, $^{42}$K, $^{64}$Cu, $^{142}$Pr |
| 2·00–5·00 | $^{37}$S, $^{38}$Cl, $^{49}$Ca | $^{56}$Mn | $^{24}$Na |
| >5·00 | $^{16}$N | | |

*d Half-lives of nuclides*

| 1–5 d | 5–30 d | 30 d–1 yr | >1 yr |
|---|---|---|---|
| $^{197}$Hg | $^{37}$Ar, $^{48}$V, $^{51}$Cr | $^{7}$Be, $^{54}$Mn, $^{58}$Co, $^{153}$Gd, $^{169}$Yb, $^{175}$Hf | $^{55}$Fe, $^{65}$Zn, $^{109}$Cd |
| $^{72}$As, $^{97}$Ru, $^{239}$Np | $^{74}$As, $^{103}$Pd | $^{75}$Se, $^{85}$Sr, $^{203}$Hg | $^{210}$Pd |
| $^{132}$Te, $^{166}$Ho | $^{131}$Ba, $^{161}$Tb, $^{234}$Th | $^{114}$In, $^{125}$I, $^{141}$Ce, $^{145}$Sm, $^{153}$Gd | $^{109}$Cd, $^{133}$Ba, $^{137}$Cs, $^{152}$Eu, $^{210}$Pb, $^{238}$Pu |
| $^{166}$Ho, $^{197}$Hg | $^{133}$Xe, $^{206}$Bi, $^{234}$Th | $^{103}$Ru, $^{169}$Yb, $^{170}$Tm, $^{175}$Hf, $^{203}$Hg | $^{22}$Na, $^{109}$Cd, $^{155}$Eu, $^{228}$Th, $^{241}$Am |
| $^{199}$Au, $^{239}$Np | $^{191}$Os | $^{57}$Co, $^{114}$In, $^{141}$Ce, $^{153}$Gd | $^{155}$Eu, $^{226}$Ra |
| $^{105}$Rh, $^{132}$Te, $^{198}$Au | $^{51}$Cr, $^{131}$I, $^{131}$Ba, $^{233}$Pa | $^{7}$Be, $^{75}$Se, $^{103}$Ru, $^{113}$Sn, $^{192}$Ir, $^{203}$Hg | $^{125}$Sb, $^{133}$Ba |
| $^{76}$As, $^{82}$Br, $^{122}$Sb | $^{74}$As, $^{140}$Ba, $^{147}$Nd | $^{46}$Sc, $^{54}$Mn, $^{85}$Sr, $^{95}$Zr/$^{95}$Nb, $^{110}$Ag, $^{124}$Sb | $^{134}$Cs, $^{137}$Cs |
| $^{47}$Ca, $^{140}$La | $^{48}$V, $^{86}$Rb | $^{46}$Sc, $^{59}$Fe, $^{65}$Zn, $^{88}$Y, $^{124}$Sb | $^{22}$Na, $^{40}$K, $^{60}$Co |

# Index